This book belongs to

....

CONTENTS

Edited by Chloe Boyes. *Designed by* Pritty Ramjee.
Cover illustrated by Stuart Trotter.
Endpapers illustrated by John Harrold.

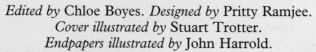

THE
RUPERT ®
ANNUAL

EXPRESS NEWSPAPERS

EGMONT
We bring stories to life

Published in Great Britain 2019 by Egmont UK Limited
The Yellow Building, 1 Nicholas Road, London W11 4AN
Rupert Bear™ & © Express Newspapers & DreamWorks Distribution Limited.
All Rights Reserved.

ISBN 978 1 4052 9444 7
70371/001
Printed in Italy

Stay safe online. Egmont is not responsible for content hosted by third parties.
Egmont takes its responsibility to the planet and its inhabitants very seriously.
We aim to use papers from well-managed forests run by responsible suppliers.

No. 84

RUPERT

Rupert and Algy call one day
On Bingo to come out to play.

Rupert and Algy call on their chum Bingo one morning, hoping he'll come out to play. They find him busy in his workshop. "Coming out to play, Bingo?" Rupert calls. "No thanks. Too busy," the clever pup shouts back. "Got to test this. Come and have a look." "A go-cart!" exclaim the others when they join Bingo. "And it's a beauty," Rupert says. Bingo grins: "Well, I must say I am rather proud of it."

and the Go-Cart

"No thanks," says Bingo. "I must start
To try out this, my new go-cart."

"A go-cart does sound lots of fun,"
Says Algy. "Why don't we build one?"

A little later Rupert and Algy are walking away from Bingo's house when Algy says, "A go-cart does sound lots of fun. Why don't we have a go at making one?" "But where do we get wood, wheels and stuff?" Rupert asks. And they are still puzzling over this when they spot the little servant of their clever friend, the Professor. "Come on!" Algy cries. "Let's ask if the Professor's got anything we could use!"

The old Professor's servant! He
May know where useful bits may be.

RUPERT IS OFFERED HELP

"Why, yes!" he gives a happy shout.
"We've lots that's due to be thrown out."

"This old shed is just full of stuff.
I feel quite sure you'll find enough."

"When his inventions fail, I fear,
He simply dumps the bits in here."

"Don't know what they're supposed to do,
But surely they'd make wheels for you."

"What a coincidence!" cries the little servant when Rupert and Algy catch up with him and ask. "The fact is, my master, the Professor, has told me to clear out a lot of stuff that's been left over from his experiments. I'm sure that among it there are bound to be wheels and wood and the like." The pals grin at each other. They can't believe their luck as the servant leads the way to a shed behind the Professor's tower home. "This place is full of stuff," he says.

And isn't he right! The pals gasp when they see inside the shed. The servant chuckles. "You know what my master's like! One experiment or invention after another. Some work, some don't. But sooner or later the parts end up here." He pauses and looks around. "Now, wheels . . ." he muses. "Ah, yes!" He rummages in a pile and comes up with two bits of machinery. "I don't know what these were meant to do," he says. "But surely they'll make wheels for you."

RUPERT SEES THE STRANGE BOX

There's lots of wood and bolts and screws,
So many things the pals can use.

"This box won't open. Still, it's neat,
And it would make a splendid seat."

A barrow's brought then so that they
Can take their go-cart stuff away.

"I think the wheels, though seeming good,
Just didn't work quite as they should."

The wheels the servant has dug out are oddly thick and have curious axles. But they look just the thing for a go-cart, Rupert and Algy agree. So now they set about looking for wood, bolts, nuts and screws to make the body. Rupert is busy dragging out several stout planks when Algy says, "Look at this box I've found. I can't open it but it's just the thing for a seat. And if the lid's nailed down as tight as all that it should be all the stronger, shouldn't it?"

At last Rupert and Algy have all they need to build a go-cart and the little servant says, "Now let's find something to carry it in." And off he goes to return with a wheelbarrow which the pals load with their stuff. "What did the Professor use all this for?" Rupert asks. "The nuts and bolts are just nuts and bolts," the servant says. "The box, I think, came from an explorer friend. The wheels . . . the Professor said something about them not working as he'd hoped."

RUPERT IS LENT A WORKSHOP

*"Round here's a workshop you may use
To build your go-cart if you choose."*

*"The old Professor's very kind.
You may be sure that he won't mind."*

*"Do use the tools but put them back,
When you are finished, in the rack."*

*"This stuff is great," says Rupert, "but
Why is this box so tightly shut?"*

Even if the wheel things didn't live up to the Professor's hopes, the pals are sure they will be just the thing for them. Now the question is, where are they going to build their go-cart? "I can help with that, too!" the servant says. "At the other end of this building is a workshop that isn't used now. I know the Professor won't mind you using it." And off he scampers ahead of the pals and their wheelbarrow to throw open the workshop doors. "There!" he announces.

The old workshop is all the two young go-cart builders could wish. "You may work here until teatime then come back tomorrow," the servant tells them. "Put the tools back neatly and lock up when you go." Then off he trots. Algy picks up one of the pairs of wheels and studies them. He spins one. "They move beautifully," he says. "And they're much lighter than they look." Rupert examines the box Algy found. "Odd that it should be nailed up so tight," he muses.

RUPERT GETS DOWN TO WORK

At once, with spanner, saw and drill,
The two pals set to with a will.

When they lock up that night they say,
They'll finish their go-cart next day.

His Mummy tells the little bear,
"It all sounds fun but do take care."

Rupert's still puzzled late that night:
"Why has that box been shut so tight?"

Now Rupert and Algy get down to work on the go-cart. They decide on a plan and measure up the wood. Then Rupert saws it into lengths and Algy drills holes to take bolts for the axles of the strange wheels. They work on steadily until their tummies tell them it's teatime. By then, all that's left to do is to put the bits together and that, they decide, can wait until tomorrow. As he locks up the shed Rupert says, "I think it's going to be better than Bingo's."

"It sounds fun," says Mrs Bear when Rupert tells his parents about the go-cart. "But are you sure the Professor won't mind you using his things?" She is quite happy, though, when Rupert assures her the things were going to be thrown out, anyway, and just says, "Well, do take care." Later in bed Rupert gets to wondering again about the box they're using as a seat. "If it's going to be thrown out why is it shut so tight?" he thinks. "Very odd, I must say."

RUPERT'S PAL TESTS THE CART

By next day, when they break to eat,
The pals' go-cart is near complete.

"My master's sure to be amused
To see how his old junk's been used."

But our two pals can't wait to start
And test their splendid new go-cart.

The cart goes well, that much is proved,
But in the seat-box something moves!

First thing next day Rupert and Algy are back in the shed to start assembling the go-cart. They've brought sandwiches so that they need not go home for lunch. In fact, by the time they come to eat them the go-cart is almost ready. When they have eaten, they fix a pair of old handles to the seat and add a steering line to the front axle. As they wheel out the finished cart the servant appears. "Oh, my master will want to see that! I'll go and fetch him," he says.

But Algy and Rupert can't wait before trying out the go-cart. "Just a short run," Algy says. "Yes, to be sure it works," Rupert grins. "You go first." So, at the top of a gentle slope, Algy seats himself on the box and takes the steering line. "Right!" Rupert cries. He pushes and away goes the go-cart, gathering speed. But when it stops at the foot of the slope Algy gets off looking thoughtful. "Something's moving in that box," he tells Ruperts as he runs up.

RUPERT TRIES IT OUT

Says Algy, "Something bumped around!"
But Rupert can't hear any sound.

"Right," Algy says, "let's see if you,
When going fast, can hear it too."

This time they use a steeper slope
To reach a greater speed, they hope.

"Hey, stop!" rings out an anxious shout.
Too late. The go-cart's now flat-out!

"Not only did something bump in the box," Algy says, "when I got up speed the wheels made a whirring sound." Rupert puts his ear to the box but he can hear nothing. "Maybe it happens only when the go-cart's moving fast," Algy suggests. "Have a go and see if you notice anything." So they take the go-cart to a steeper slope where it should go even faster. As he gets ready Rupert remembers his earlier puzzlement about the box being shut so tight. But just then Algy cries,

"Ready!", gives a push and away races the go-cart. For a moment the speed is almost frightening, then just as Rupert starts to enjoy it, three things happen. From inside the box comes a very definite bump. The wheels start to whirr louder and louder. And from somewhere behind him Rupert hears the frantic voices of the Professor and his servant shouting for him to stop. That's much easier said than done, for now the go-cart is going flat-out!

RUPERT TAKES OFF

Each of the go-cart's four wheels whirrs
And in the seat-box something stirs!

A cliff-top looms! No time to steer!
He's on the edge – and racing clear!

Now Rupert sees the reason why
There was no crash – the cart can fly!

The clever old Professor's made
Each wheel a sort of rotor-blade!

Now everything's happening far too fast – the wheels whirring louder than ever, the Professor shouting, the bumping inside the box and the awful thought that in their hurry, Algy and he have fitted no brakes to the go-cart! Suddenly the whirring stops and, open-mouthed, Rupert sees the wheels begin to open like umbrellas! At the same moment he sees he is headed for a small cliff. No time to steer away from it! Next instant the go-cart sails over the edge of the cliff.

Rupert braces himself for a crash. But there is none – for the go-cart is flying! The wheels have opened completely and turned on their sides, whirring away like the rotor-blades of a helicopter. Rupert clings to the handles and holds his breath. But nothing awful happens. The wheels spin on, carrying the go-cart smoothly through the air just clear of the treetops. "I say," thinks Rupert. "I'm beginning to enjoy this, after all."

RUPERT THINKS HE SHOULD LAND

Now Rupert laughs, "I think I'll start
To call this thing my helicart!"

But Rupert's fun does not last long.
Once more that bumping! This time strong.

Below he sees his little band
Of friends and thinks, "I'd better land."

"Land? Oh, dear, I don't know how,
And, gosh, the bumping's much worse now!"

In no time at all Rupert begins to feel quite chirpy. He even makes a little joke – "I think I'll call this my helicart." He feels confident enough to let go of the handles and take up the steering line. He tries steering and it works. "I'll steer as far as Podgy's house," he decides. "Then I'll turn round." But it is just as he is rounding the forest that the bumping starts inside the box again. This time, though, it is much stronger! Rupert is not too worried about this because the go-cart is still flying well. He turns back to where he started and there, above the little cliff, he sees his three friends gazing up at him. The Professor seems to be shouting and Rupert remembers how, just before the go-cart took off, the Professor was trying to stop him. "I'd better land," he thinks. And with a shock he realises he doesn't know how to land! At that moment the bumping in the box becomes frighteningly stronger.

It's just as well he cannot hear
The old Professor's cries of fear.

By now the bumping is so bad,
That just to keep his seat he's glad.

Then suddenly all four wheels stop!
The helicart begins to drop!

Still louder comes the bumping sound,
As Rupert plummets to the ground.

It's just as well that Rupert can't hear what the Professor is shouting which is, "Come down at once – you are in great danger!" Already he is quite scared enough and, anyway, he doesn't know how to bring the go-cart down. From inside the box comes a growing bump – bump – bump, and it shakes so much that Rupert has to grab a handle to stay put. "How am I going to land?" he quavers. Then he gives a cry of alarm, for he has just seen how he is likely to get down! The wheels which have been keeping the go-cart in the air have stopped! The go-cart slows. The rush of air dies away. The only sound comes from the box. Bump – bump – bump! Louder and stronger than ever. Then down drops the go-cart, so suddenly that it almost leaves poor Rupert behind. But he is clinging to the handles just as hard as he can and goes with it. Down – down – down the go-cart plummets. As the ground rushes up to meet it Rupert shuts his eyes.

RUPERT IS SAVED

Aghast, his poor friends watch the fall.
There's nothing they can do at all.

But now what's happening to the cart?
The seat-box seems to fly apart!

Two strange wings pop out from inside.
The cart's fall stops and down they glide.

As Rupert's craft comes in to land
His friends rush up to lend a hand.

On the ground Rupert's horrified friends watch the go-cart falling. There is not a thing they can do. Eyes shut tight, Rupert clings to the handles. He can't think. Just wait for the awful . . . hello! What's happening? The bumping inside the box is frantic now. It's as if the box is going to tear itself apart. Cre-e-eak! Crack! Rupert risks opening an eye. Bits of wood fly past his face. But wait! The go-cart is not falling. It seems to be flying again!

Rupert opens both eyes. Then he opens them really wide, astounded by what he sees. The go-cart is flying. But the wheels are still not working. And from holes in the side of the box protrude two wings. Such wings! They are like no bird's wings Rupert has ever seen. They look webbed and leathery, more like a bat's than a bird's. But they are plainly strong wings, for beating with a slow steady stroke, they carry the go-cart in a glide towards the ground.

RUPERT SEES WHAT SAVED THEM

Whatever's in the box can't see,
And so lands rather clumsily.

His friends help up the little bear,
But half-way, stop and gasp and stare!

And Rupert can't believe his eyes.
"Is that some sort of bird?" he cries.

The old man breathes, "I do declare,
That is a pterodactyl there!"

Whatever is in the box plainly can't see where it is flying, Rupert realises, and so, as the ground approaches he gets ready for the big bump. In fact, it isn't awful, but still enough to throw him clear of the go-cart. "Rupert, are you all right?" It is Algy who is first to reach the scene. The others are close behind him. They are helping Rupert to his feet when he realises that they aren't looking at him. They are staring at something behind him.

He swings round to see what and his own eyes pop at the sight that greets them. The top has come off the box and sticking up is the head of the wings' owner. It looks something like a bird's head, but it has a sort of horn sticking out behind on which is balanced a bit of egg-shell. The Professor is the first to speak: "I do declare, it's a pterodactyl! A real life pterodactyl!" The others stare at it in silence. Then Rupert whispers, "It's a terry-what?"

RUPERT PICKS A NAME

The creature is the strangest thing
With sort of fingers on each wing.

"Let's call it Terry, if we may.
Its proper name is hard to say."

"Terry? Why, yes! I think that's neat.
Let's take him home. He'll want to eat."

"I say!" laughs Algy. "Look at that!
He's hanging there just like a bat!"

"It is a pterodactyl," repeats the Professor and spells out the word. "You say it 'terrodaktil'," he adds. "But let's get the poor little thing out of there." And he and his servant set about gently releasing the creature from the box. It seems very friendly. "What is a ... what you called it?" Rupert asks. "Well," says the Professor, "pterodactyls are flying creatures which vanished from the earth thousands of years ago – or so we thought."

"Since its name's so hard to say," Rupert suggests, "why don't we call it simply Terry?" "H'm, Terry the pterodactyl," muses the Professor. "Yes, that's neat. Terry it shall be. Now let's get him home and find him something to eat." He picks up a fallen branch and, with his servant, holds it out to Terry who seems to know what's wanted for he hops onto it and hangs upside down. "Just like a bat!" laughs Algy. Then off they all set for the Professor's tower.

RUPERT MEETS A SARDINE LOVER

*"Find out if we've got what we need
To make up pterodactyl feed."*

*The old man is explaining when
His servant hurries in again.*

*"I let the little creature taste
All sorts of things. But what a waste!"*

*"He tried spaghetti, crisps and beans
But all he likes are tinned sardines."*

Indoors Terry is taken off in search of whatever food pterodactyls may eat. "What an adventure!" the Professor chuckles when he and the others are settled in his study. "All because of my old junk. I made the wheels for a flying trolley. But they didn't work well. The egg came from an explorer friend who found it somewhere. Who'd have thought it would hatch? My servant must have thrown the box out thinking it was empty." And just then the servant returns. "I've found what Terry likes," he announces. Seemingly he tried all sorts of food on the little creature without success – until he tried sardines. "He's eaten six lots," the servant says. "I'd a job to stop him eating the tins!" The Professor smiles. "We shall have to find a place suitable for pterodactyls," he says. "But until we do – and that could take time – Terry can stay here. At least we know what to feed him on!"
THE END

RUPERT
and the
Skylark

RUPERT FINDS A STRANGE SHOE

"Hurrah!" smiles Rupert. "Spring is here.
The Winter's over, till next year!"

"A bird!" he thinks. "I wonder why
It's landed? It's too tired to fly!"

"It's not a bird at all!" he thinks.
"It's someone's sandal!" Rupert blinks.

"But where's it from?" He tries to guess.
"It's Ottoline's – her fancy dress!"

It is a sunny Spring morning in Nutwood and Rupert has decided to go for a walk across the common. "Thank goodness Winter is finally over!" he smiles. "I was beginning to think it would never end!" Everywhere Rupert looks he sees flowers blooming, trees coming into leaf and birds returning from their Winter migration. All of a sudden, he spots a strange bird lying in a clump of long grass. "I hope it's all right!" he blinks. "Perhaps it's exhausted from flying so far . . ."

Trying not to startle the bird, Rupert tip-toes forward to take a closer look . . . "I don't believe it!" he laughs. "It isn't a bird at all! Somebody's lost a sandal. It's like an ordinary shoe, but with wings!" As he looks at the sandal, Rupert wonders where it can have come from. "It must be part of somebody's fancy dress costume!" he smiles. "Ottoline, I expect! She's always dressing up in old-fashioned clothes. I suppose she dropped it on her way across the common . . ."

RUPERT MAKES A DISCOVERY

Before he goes on Rupert tries
The sandal that he's found for size . . .

He feels a tingle in his toes –
"It's from the sandal I suppose!"

With every step that Rupert takes
He marvels at the leaps he makes . . .

"The sandal's feathers must be why
I'm able to jump up so high."

As Rupert looks more closely at the sandal, it seems too big to belong to Ottoline. "It fits over the top of my shoe!" he blinks. "I wonder what it's like to wear?" Buckling the sandal, he feels his foot start to tingle, almost as though he is being tickled. "How odd!" he murmurs. "I wonder if it's something to do with the feathers?" When Rupert tries walking he gets another surprise. "It's springy!" he gasps. "I can bounce up and down like a pogo-stick!"

With the winged sandal on his foot, Rupert finds he can jump higher and higher. "This is fun!" he laughs. "I feel as though I could hop all the way across the common . . ." Before long, he reaches a little stream. Although it would normally be too wide to cross, he takes a flying jump and clears it in a single bound! As Rupert's balance improves, he finds he can jump even higher, leaping over rocks and bushes without any trouble at all. "I feel as if I could fly!" he marvels.

RUPERT MEETS A STRANGER

The running jump that Rupert tries,
Is so enormous that he flies!

To his astonishment he sees
A stranger, high above the trees . . .

"Hello, there!" Rupert gives a yell –
"I'm up above the trees as well!"

The boy has a winged sandal, too –
"What luck!" he laughs. "You've found my shoe!"

As soon as Rupert starts to think about flying, he finds himself being lifted off the ground and up into the air. "It must be magic!" he gasps. "This sandal will take me wherever I want to go!" Drifting higher, Rupert soon reaches the edge of Nutwood forest. "Amazing!" he gasps as he looks down to see the trees spread out below, like a huge, green carpet. As Rupert turns round he suddenly spots a distant figure. "There's somebody else up here!" he blinks. "They can fly as well!"

Rupert calls across the treetops to the distant figure, who spins round in surprise, then hurries over to join him. At first he thinks it must be Jack Frost but, as the boy gets nearer, Rupert sees it is a stranger, dressed in a colourful costume trimmed with feathers. "Hello!" he smiles. "You've found my sandal!" "Yes," nods Rupert. "I hope you don't mind me trying it out." "No!" laughs the boy. "I can still fly with one shoe but I never thought that anyone else would learn the same trick!"

RUPERT FOLLOWS THE SKYLARK

The boy asks Rupert where they are –
"Are you from Nutwood? Is it far?"

"My cousin Jack comes every year,
He thought that I might like it here . . ."

"Come on!" the Skylark gives a cry.
"It's fun to play when you can fly!"

He swoops to earth and grabs a stick –
"Just what we need to play a trick . . ."

"Do you live in Nutwood?" asks the boy. "Yes," says Rupert. "I was crossing the common when I found your sandal." "It must have fallen off while I was practising somersaults!" laughs Rupert's new friend. "I flew here with the birds! My cousin said I'd like it. He comes to Nutwood to collect your snowmen . . ." "Snowmen?" blinks Rupert. "But that must be Jack Frost!" "That's right!" nods the boy. "I'm his cousin, Skylark. I live near the equator, where your birds go in the winter . . ."

Now that he has found the sandal's owner, Rupert offers to return it straightaway. "No, no!" laughs Skylark. "You won't be able to fly if you take it off. I've come to Nutwood to have some fun. There are all sorts of games we can play if we can both fly . . ." Swooping down towards Nutwood's lake, he picks up a fallen branch with a whoop of delight. "Perfect!" he cries. "I'll show you how to write on water!" "Water?" blinks Rupert. "Follow me!" calls Skylark. "Over the lake . . ."

RUPERT WALKS A TIGHTROPE

The boy starts drawing on the lake –
"Look, Rupert! It's a watersnake!"

"We'll try a new game now! Let's see . . .
That clothes-line will do perfectly!"

"It's time to learn a new trick now –
Tightrope walking! I'll show you how . . ."

"Just don't look down! You're doing fine!"
He calls as Rupert walks the line.

As Rupert looks on, Skylark hovers over the surface of the lake and stirs the water with the tip of his stick. "Amazing!" gasps Rupert. "I can see what you're drawing!" "A watersnake!" laughs the boy as Nutwood's ducks flap their wings. "Now let's find a new game to play." Flying towards Nutwood, he catches sight of Mrs Sheep's cottage. "Look at that clothes-line!" Skylark chuckles. "The garden's empty. No one's about. It's too good to miss." "What do you mean?" blinks Rupert.

To Rupert's surprise, Skylark flies down to Mrs Sheep's garden and starts skipping along the washing-line, like a tightrope walker . . . "Come on!" he cries. "You should be able to do this too, now you can fly." Rupert puts one foot on the line, then steps forward gingerly. "Don't look down!" calls Skylark. "Just follow me across. You'll soon get the hang of it!" "You're right!" laughs Rupert. "No wonder you like playing games! If I could fly, I'd be able to do tricks like this all the time!"

RUPERT'S PAL PLANS A NEW TRICK

"Bless me!" blinks Mrs Sheep. "You two
Are flying! No, it can't be true . . ."

The Skylark hurries on his way –
"A farm! Now that's the place to play!"

"Oh, dear!" thinks Rupert anxiously . . .
"Whatever will his next trick be?"

"A weathervane!" the Skylark cries.
"Let's find out how well this one flies . . ."

Just as Rupert gets to the end of the washing line, he suddenly hears somebody call his name. "Rupert!" cries Mrs Sheep. "Fancy you being able to walk the tightrope! I couldn't believe my eyes!" "I hope you don't mind us using your clothes line . . ." starts Rupert, but Skylark is already over the hedge and off in search of new adventures. "Wait!" calls Rupert as he hurries after his new chum. "Come on!" cries Skylark. "I can see a farm. There'll be lots to do there . . ."

Rupert chases after Skylark, anxiously wondering what he plans to get up to at Farmer Brown's. "A weathervane!" the prankster cries. "I knew we'd find one somewhere!" It is a quiet day and the farm seems deserted as the pair hover up above the rooftops. "Farmer Brown must be out on his rounds," thinks Rupert, with a sign of relief. "Have you ever seen a weathervane fly?" asks Skylark. "No," says Rupert. "I thought they stayed where they were." "Not always!" smiles the Lark.

RUPERT SEES A WEATHERVANE FLY

"We'll see who spins the tin bird best –
Through four points – North, South, East and West!"

The cockerel spins so violently
It leaves its old perch and breaks free . . .

"Oh, no!" gasps Rupert in dismay –
"The weathervane's flying away!"

But Skylark doesn't seem to care –
He's off to try another dare . . .

"Watch!" calls Skylark. "We'll have a competition to see who can make it go fastest . . ." Seizing the weathervane by the tail, he spins it round as if a hurricane was blowing. "Stop!" cries Rupert. "You'll make it dizzy!" "Nonsense!" laughs his companion. "They're meant to go round and round. As he speaks, the weathervane suddenly breaks free from its perch and shoots up into the air. "Now look what you've done!" gasps Rupert. "Gosh!" blinks Skylark. "I've never seen that before!" To Rupert's amazement the weathervane gives an angry squawk, flaps its metal wings and flies off over the fields. "It's leaving!" he gasps. "Farmer Brown will be furious when he finds out what has happened!" "Farmer Brown?" asks Skylark. "Is he the man walking past the barn?" "Yes," groans Rupert. "If he sees the weathercock flying off it will make things even worse!" "Don't fuss!" says Skylark. "Silly old farmers don't worry me! Let's see if he wants to join the fun!"

RUPERT'S PAL TEASES THE FARMER

"Hats off!" cries Skylark, swooping down
To play a trick on Farmer Brown . . .

"What fun!" he laughs. "Did you see that?
Now, what shall we do with this hat?"

"Scamp!" calls the farmer angrily.
"Just throw that hat back down to me!"

The hat lands on its owner's head –
"Let's find another game instead!"

"Hats off!" cries Skylark, swooping down towards Farmer Brown. To Rupert's horror, he snatches the farmer's hat and flies up with a whoop. At first, Farmer Brown thinks his hat has been blown off by the wind. He looks round, then catches sight of Rupert and Skylark, hovering over his head. "Rupert!" he cries. "What's going on? Who's that holding my hat?" "What fun!" laughs Skylark. "Now, where shall I put this? Perhaps the treetops? We could see how long it takes to blow down . . ." "Give back that hat, you scallywag!" calls Farmer Brown. "I don't mind a joke but you've gone too far." "All right!" says the prankster. "Stand still and I'll see what I can do!" Taking careful aim, he throws the hat down towards the farmer, like a ring at a hoop-la stall. "Bull's-eye!" he laughs as it lands on Farmer Brown's head. "You can't complain about that, can you? Come on, Rupert. Let's go and find something else to play. There's lots of Nutwood I haven't seen yet!"

RUPERT'S FRIENDS ARE ANNOYED

"A football match! Let's join in too!
Your friends won't mind if I'm with you . . ."

The pals are all astonished by
The figure swooping from the sky . . .

"Catch!" calls the Skylark. "We can throw
The ball between us – to and fro . . ."

But Rupert flies back down to where
His startled pals all stand and stare.

Leaving the farm behind them, Rupert and Skylark fly over Nutwood Common until they spot a group of chums playing football. "That looks fun!" says the visitor. "Do you think they'll mind if I join in?" "Of course not," says Rupert. "Although we'd better land out of sight so they aren't too startled." "Land?" laughs Skylark. "But that would spoil the game . . ." As Rupert looks on, his companion swoops down and catches the ball in mid-air. "Hey!" gasps Algy. "What's the big idea?" "Catch!" calls Skylark, throwing the pals' ball to Rupert. "We'll have a game of Piggy in the Middle." "No you won't!" cries Algy. "Give us back our ball! Come on, Rupert! I don't know who your new friend is, but I don't think much of his manners." "Sorry!" says Rupert, drifting down to join his chums. "He was only having fun. I'm sure he didn't mean to spoil your game." "You're flying too!" blinks Willie. "What's going on? It must be magic! Or are we all dreaming?"

RUPERT CHASES THE SKYLARK

"This boy's called Skylark, everyone –
He likes to play jokes and have fun . . ."

"Come on!" calls Skylark. "Time to play!"
He snatches Rupert's scarf away . . .

"Hey!" Rupert calls. "Give that to me!"
The boy just gives a cry of glee . . .

He flies off high above the ground
Towards an ancient tower he's found . . .

Handing Algy the ball, Rupert tells his chums the whole story of how he found the winged sandal, then met its mischievous owner. "He's called Skylark," Rupert explains. "And he loves playing jokes and pranks! At first it was fun, but the trouble is, he just doesn't know when to stop . . ." As Rupert speaks, he suddenly feels someone tugging at his scarf. "Come on!" laughs Skylark. "Don't be a spoilsport! Let's play something else. How about Hide and Seek?"

"Hey! Come back with my scarf!" calls Rupert. "Catch me if you can!" laughs Skylark, bounding off over the fields. "Come back!" cries Rupert, but the boy flies over the treetops, trailing the scarf behind. "I'd better not let him out of sight!" thinks Rupert. As the pair reach the edge of the common, Skylark spots the Old Professor's tower. "Oh, no!" groans Rupert. "I hope there aren't any windows open. If he gets his hands on one of the Professor's machines, who knows what might happen?"

31

RUPERT ASTONISHES BODKIN

"Come on!" calls Skylark. "Now let's see
How fast you are. Catch up with me!"

"Wait! Skylark!" Rupert gives a shout
As Bodkin happens to look out . . .

"Amazing!" Bodkin blinks. "I'm sure
I've never seen you fly before!"

Rupert starts to explain, but then
The Skylark flies off once again.

As the pair near the Professor's tower, Skylark glances over his shoulder and catches sight of Rupert. "Come on, slowcoach!" he calls. "You'll never catch me like that!" Before Rupert can answer, his new pal disappears from sight behind the ivy-clad building. "You'll have to be quick to catch me!" calls the boy. "My next hiding place will be *much* harder to find." As Rupert circles round the tower, an astonished Bodkin appears at the window and looks out to see who's there . . .

"Rupert!" cries Bodkin. "I thought I heard your voice. What are you doing?" "Chasing someone!" calls Rupert. "I can't stop to explain or they'll get away . . ." "He's flying too!" gasps Bodkin. "I've never seen anything like it!" Leaving the tower behind, Rupert follows Skylark over the fields surrounding Nutwood and up towards a ridge of rocky hills. "I wonder where he's heading for?" he murmurs. "If we keep going this way we'll end up by the coast. I do hope Skylark stops soon . . ."

RUPERT FINDS SKYLARK

As Rupert thinks he's drawing near,
The Skylark seems to disappear!

"He's hiding!" Rupert thinks, "But where?
I know! I'll try that nest, up there . . ."

"Well done!" laughs Skylark. "Let's see how
You get on – hiding from me now . . ."

But, suddenly, an eagle flies
Towards the nest. "Help!" Skylark cries.

Suddenly, as Rupert chases after him, Skylark seems to vanish . . . "I wonder where he's gone?" Rupert thinks. "He must be hiding somewhere. Perhaps at the top of one of those tall trees . . ." Rupert searches the tree-tops carefully, but, to his surprise, there is no sign of the prankster to be seen. "What now?" Rupert sighs. "I can't fly back to Nutwood and leave him behind . . ." Just then, the sound of giggling breaks the silence. "Skylark!" thinks Rupert. "He must be in that empty nest."

"Here I am!" laughs Skylark, popping up from the nest. "I was beginning to think you'd never find me . . ." "I didn't know we'd started!" says Rupert. "I suppose it's my turn to hide now?" "That's right!" says his friend. "I'll close my eyes and count to one hundred. You'll have to choose well though, hide and seek is one of my favourite games!" Just then, a shadow sweeps over the nest and a huge eagle swoops down towards the startled pair. "Help!" cries Skylark, but it is too late . . .

RUPERT SEES SKYLARK CARRIED OFF

The bird swoops down to seize its prey,
Then carries Rupert's chum away!

"Wait!" Skylark calls. "I didn't know
It was your nest. Please let me go!"

The bird speeds off as Rupert tries
To keep an eye on where it flies . . .

He sees the eagle gaining height,
Then cloud banks hide the bird from sight!

With an angry cry, the giant eagle seizes Skylark and lifts him out of the nest . . . clutching him in its mighty talons, it flaps its wings and soars up into the sky. "Wait!" calls the boy. "I didn't know it was your nest! We were only playing a game!" Ignoring his protests, the great bird flies on, over the tree-tops towards the distant hills. "Don't worry!" calls Rupert. "I'm sure it will let you go soon. Perhaps it thinks you're some sort of baby bird . . ."

Rupert follows the eagle away from Nutwood and over the rocky hills. "I wonder where it's taking Skylark?" he thinks. "I'll try to keep as close as I can, so I see where it goes . . ." To Rupert's surprise, the great bird starts to climb higher and higher, up towards the clouds. "Perhaps it doesn't live here at all!" he thinks. "The nest might belong to another bird . . ." Next moment, the bird is lost from sight as it soars above a heavy bank of cloud, leaving Rupert far below . . .

RUPERT VISITS THE BIRD KING

The eagle soars through clouds to fly
Towards a castle in the sky . . .

"The Bird King's Palace!" Rupert blinks.
"They've gone to see the King!" he thinks.

"The weathervane! I might have known
That this is where it would have flown . . ."

The King says, "I take a dim view
Of people playing tricks, like you . . ."

Climbing higher and higher, Rupert passes through a misty patch of cloud then suddenly spots the towers of a castle in the sky. "Of course!" he gasps. "That's where the eagle's heading for! He's taking Skylark to the Bird King's palace . . ." Although Rupert has visited the palace before, the birds are clearly astonished to see him hovering in mid-air. "Can you take me to the King?" he asks as they fly round excitedly. "I think he has just had some other visitors from Nutwood . . ."

As Rupert lands in the castle courtyard, he can see Skylark being questioned by the King, with the eagle looking on sternly. "The weathervane's there too!" he gasps. "It must have flown straight from Nutwood to complain about being spun round!" "These are serious charges!" the King declares as Rupert draws near. "Your winged sandals make you a particular menace to creatures of the air. I shall have to send a formal complaint to your mother. It might be better if you were grounded for good!"

RUPERT ASKS FOR MERCY

"Wait!" Rupert calls. "Your Majesty,
"Don't act until you've heard my plea . . ."

"I know that Skylark caused alarm,
But all his high jinks meant no harm."

A parrot speaks for Skylark too –
"A harmless prankster, Sire! It's true!"

The King agrees to let things go –
"No more wild jokes from now on, though!"

"Wait!" calls Rupert, interrupting the King. "Please don't be too harsh on him . . ." "Rupert?" blinks the toucan. "You *know* this miscreant? You may speak on his behalf, if you wish, but the charges against him are very grave!" "I know!" says Rupert. "Skylark has done a lot of bad things, but I'm sure he didn't mean any harm." "Really?" says the King. "I take a dim view of people who play pranks on weathervanes, not to mention trespassing in other birds' nests . . ."

As Rupert is talking to the King, a brightly coloured parrot flies up to join them. "Please, Sire!" it squawks. "I can vouch for Skylark too! He lives in the forests of the South, with birds and animals as his play-fellows. He's a bit boisterous sometimes, but I know he'd never harm another creature!" "Well, well!" murmurs the King. "This does rather change things . . ." Turning to Skylark, he announces a Royal Pardon for past misdemeanours. "We'll let you make a fresh start!"

RUPERT'S PAL IS FORGIVEN

"I'm sorry for the harm I've done!
I'll make it up to everyone . . ."

The boy declares he'd like to stay
In Nutwood for another day . . .

The weathervane befriends the pair –
"It's been fun, taking to the air."

He shows the chums which way to go –
"Directions are my job, you know!"

Thanking the King, Skylark turns to the weathervane and apologises for spinning it off its perch. "I won't do it again!" he promises. "Good!" says the bird. "In that case, we can all be friends." As the weathervane speaks, Skylark has a sudden idea. "I'd like to go back to Nutwood, if you don't mind," he tells the King. "There's something else I have to do before I go home." "Very well," agrees the King. "You can all fly there together, with the weathervane as your guide . . ."

As soon as they have said goodbye to the King, Rupert and Skylark take to the air, together with the weathervane. "What an adventure!" it laughs. "It's the first time I've left Nutwood for years! Suppose I've got *you* to thank for that, young man!" Skylark is amazed by how quickly the bird finds its way back to Nutwood. "Easy, when you know how!" it preens. "North, South, East, West. Finding the way is what I do best! All you have to do is fly in the right direction . . ."

37

"We're home!" the vane crows in delight
As Nutwood's fields come into sight . . .

It flies back to its perch and then
Sits motionless and still again!

Skylark flies on until he comes
Across a group of Rupert's chums . . .

"Hello!" he smiles. "I've come to see
If you'd all like to play with me!"

Following the weathervane over hills and fields, Rupert and Skylark finally come to the outskirts of Nutwood and Farmer Brown's barn . . . "Goodbye!" calls their guide. "I'd better get back now, before I'm missed!" Flying down to the farm, it perches above the wind-vane and folds its wings. "Just like it was before!" laughs Skylark. "I never knew they could really fly . . ." "Me neither!" says Rupert. "I don't suppose I'd ever have found out if it hadn't been for you . . ."

Leaving the farm, Skylark flies on across Nutwood Common until he spots a group of Rupert's chums. "They're the reason I've come back," he says. "I want to make up for spoiling their game of football . . ." At first, the pals are rather wary of Rupert's companion, but when they hear that he wants to be friends, they soon agree to let bygones be bygones. "I wish *I* could fly like you!" says Bill. "You can!" laughs Skylark. "All you have to do is borrow one of my sandals . . ."

RUPERT'S CHUMS TRY FLYING TOO

The chums each take a turn to try
The magic shoes which make you fly . . .

"It's fun to play with friends, like you,
I wish I lived in Nutwood too!"

All Rupert's pals thank Skylark for
The game and ask him back once more . . .

"Goodbye!" calls Rupert. "For today –
I'm sure you'll soon be back this way!"

To the chums' delight, Skylark offers them a chance to try his sandals too . . . "You'll soon get the hang of flying!" he smiles. "It's amazing!" laughs Bill. "I feel as though I'm swimming through air . . ." "Watch me!" cries Algy. "My turn next!" calls Willie Mouse. "I'm glad they're enjoying themselves!" Skylark tells Rupert. "It must be nice to have so many friends . . ." "Haven't you?" asks Rupert. "No!" sighs the boy. "Birds, and monkeys sometimes, but no-one like you!"

At last, the fun ends and the pals return the magic sandals . . . "Thank you for coming back!" says Willie. "I hope you'll visit us again . . ." "Do you think I could?" says Skylark happily. "That would be marvellous!" "Of course!" smiles Rupert. "You can visit Nutwood whenever you like." "I will!" laughs the boy. "And now, I'd better be on my way! Thanks, everyone!" "Goodbye!" calls Rupert as Skylark sets off. "See you soon . . ." THE END

RUPERT and

On such a day of wind and sun
You need a chum to share the fun.

Sunshine and wind! The sort of day for exploring the countryside around Nutwood; when you almost wish an adventure would happen. "It would be nicer, though if I'd a pal with me," thinks Rupert as he crosses the common. Then – "Hello, Rupert!" The squeaky greeting comes from a small animal under a bush. "Horace Hedgehog!" exclaims Rupert. "I didn't see you." "But I heard you," Horace says. "Thinking aloud."

the Wonderful Kite

Horace the Hedgehog says, "Nearby
You should find Bill. Give him a try."

He hurries down and takes a peep,
And there's Bill fishing – fast asleep!

Rupert laughs: "Yes, I was thinking what a splendid day it is, but not so much fun on your own." "You're in luck," Horace says. "Bill Badger is fishing near here. Try him." Rupert thanks Horace and heads for the stream. Sure enough, there's Bill on a plank over the water, fishing-rod in hand . . . fast asleep. "Lazy Bill," Rupert chuckles. "I'll show him." He steals up, lifts out the line and fixes his handkerchief to it.

So Rupert steals down to the brook
And ties his hankie to Bill's hook.

"I say, I've got a bite!" Bill cries,
Then almost falls in with surprise.

"In fact that fishing was a bore,"
Bill says. "Come on, let us explore!"

As often happens in such gales,
Over a hedge someone's hat sails.

It bowls along as if alive
Until Bill traps it with a dive.

Rupert tugs the handkerchief. Bill wakes with a start. "I've got a bite!" he cries. He pulls in his line and finds . . . a handkerchief. "What?" he begins then swings round, nearly falling off the plank when Rupert bursts out laughing. But being Bill he shares the joke and when Rupert asks him to come exploring he says he'd love to and that he was getting bored anyway. So off they go, arm in arm, both with a feeling that some adventure lies ahead.

As the pals press on the wind gets stronger. Bushes flail and trees shake. "This sort of wind brings down chimney pots!" Bill says. "And look, there goes one now!" Rupert sees the round, black thing soar over the bushes. "No, it's a hat!" he cries. "After it, Bill!" Laughing, they chase the hat across the field. Each time they think they have it a gust blows it out of reach again. Then at last Bill catches it with a tremendous flying tackle.

RUPERT MEETS THE HAT'S OWNER

Bill tries the hat. It hides his eyes.
"Let's play a game then!" Rupert cries.

Then at the gate a man appears.
It's his hat they have, Rupert fears.

The man's not cross. He doesn't mind.
"You caught my hat," he says. "How kind!"

"For saving my old hat from harm
I'll show you two around my farm."

"Go on, Bill, try it on!" Rupert grins. Bill jams the hat over his head. "I can't see a thing!" he laughs with the brim resting on his nose. "I know, then!" cries Rupert. "Let's play hide and seek." But they have hardly begun to play when a shout stops them. Bill whips off the hat. A man is waving at them. "I say, I rather think it's his hat we've got," Rupert whispers as the man beckons to them. "Come on, we'd better take it back to him quick."

Wondering if the man saw them playing about with his hat, Rupert and Bill approach nervously. But as they get near they see that he is smiling. If he has seen them larking with his hat he doesn't mention it. Instead he says, "That was kind of you to catch my hat. It's old but I'm fond of it." He turns out to be a farmer and when he learns that the pals like farms he shows them around his. When they have seen everything he asks, "Hungry, eh? Then how about some lunch?"

RUPERT IS GIVEN THE KITE

They lunch and then he tells the two,
"Up here I've a surprise for you."

"Oh what a mess!" he says. "Oh dear!
But I'm quite sure it's somewhere here."

"Yes, here it is, my good old kite!"
The pals accept it with delight.

As off they go their friend reveals
The kite has some strange power, he feels.

After a delicious lunch the farmer says, "Now I have a surprise for you. Follow me." He leads Rupert and Bill through the old farmhouse and up a twisty flight of stairs to a loft, cluttered with all sorts of things. "Now, I'm sure it's hereabouts somewhere," he mutters, gazing around at the mass of trunks and crates and boxes. The pals exchange looks. What can he be looking for? Then – "Aha! There it is!" cries the farmer and plunges among some packing cases.

What he produces is a kite. It's a good one, old but beautifully made. "Here you are," he says. "A 'thank-you' present for saving my hat." The delighted chums thank him over and over as they carry the kite down from the loft. "Just one thing," says the farmer. "I've heard it said this old kite has magic powers. I don't know for sure, but it's led me into one or two strange adventures." Excitedly Rupert and Bill rush outside to try their new present.

RUPERT LOSES THE KITE

By now the wind has grown so strong,
Quite helpless, Rupert's dragged along.

Bill lends a hand. They tug and, oh!
The kite string snaps and down they go.

And off it soars, their lovely kite!
They try to keep the thing in sight.

They saw it come down in some trees,
And think they'll find the spot with ease.

How that kite can fly! In the strong wind it soars like a great bird, dragging Rupert along, panting and stumbling with Bill racing behind. Soon they are on high ground where the wind is even stronger. "I-I can't hold it on my own!" pants Rupert. "Come on, Bill, give me a hand with it!" Bill grabs hold of the line and the two throw their full weight backwards. For a moment it seems that they can hold the kite, then – ping! – the line snaps.

Off soars the kite, free of the line. "For goodness' sake, don't lose sight of it, Bill!" Rupert shouts as they pick themselves up. From the top of the hill they watch their new present dwindle into the distance . . . then suddenly it plunges into a wood. "After it!" cries Rupert. "I think I saw where it came down." They race down the hill and into the wood. But there, in among the thick trees and the bushes, finding the kite doesn't seem nearly so easy.

RUPERT IS LED TO THE KITE

But no, the wood's too dense and they
Soon find that they have lost their way.

Just then they see a bird alight.
It knows where they can find their kite.

"Behind that wall's a garden fair.
And you will find your kite in there."

But when at last the door swings wide
A grumpy old man stands inside.

Deeper and deeper into the woods push the two chums. At last Bill stops, leans against a tree and wipes his forehead. "I'm lost. I've no idea which way we're going even. I don't think we're going to find the kite, do you?" Glumly Rupert shakes his head. "Kite?" says a tweetery voice. "Are you two looking for a kite?" The speaker is a bird perched on a tree stump. At once the pals are alert again. "I've seen a kite," says the bird. "Follow me. I'll show you where."

Hardly able to believe their good luck, Rupert and Bill follow the bird through the trees. It stops at last before a high stone wall with a door in it. "Your kite fell into the garden behind this wall," chirps the bird. "Good luck!" "Good luck? That's an odd thing to say," Rupert thinks. But the bird has already gone. Now Bill reaches for the bell-pull beside the door and tugs. After what seems a long time the door is opened by a scowling old man.

"I'll have no strangers nose about
In here," the old man snarls. "Get out!"

The two chums turn and seem to flee.
But stop and hide behind a tree.

They circle all around that wall.
But everywhere it's far too tall.

"Bill, just a moment!" Rupert cries.
"Our way in through that tunnel lies."

"M-may we come in and get our kite?" Rupert quavers. "Come in?" repeats the old man, and he scowls more fiercely than ever. "Come in? Never! You get away from here and stay away. Don't want any nosey strangers prowling round here. Now get out!" And to the pals' alarm he produces a stick from behind his back and waves it at them. They turn and run . . . but only as far as a big tree behind which they hide until the old man goes growling back into the mysterious garden.

"Let's see if we can find some other way of getting inside," Rupert says. So they set off following the wall. But everywhere it is high and even if they could climb it they can see they would be stopped by the spikes on top. "It looks as if we've lost our kite for good," Bill says dismally. And it is just at that moment that Rupert spies a possible way in – a tunnel that allows a small stream to run under the wall and in to the garden.

RUPERT SAILS THROUGH

"Yes, that's it, Rupert! Good for you!"
Bill cries. "But how do we get through?"

No need for them to swim or wade,
They'll use the tree trunk as an aid.

"I'll make the log secure. We may
Just need it to come back this way."

They board the log, they cower low,
Then underneath the wall they go.

"But how do we get through it?" Bill wants to know. "Swim? We could. It looks pretty short." "I've a better idea," Rupert says. "That log over there." He points to a length of tree trunk on the bank. "Give me a hand to get it into the water." "You mean we float through the tunnel on it?" Bill exclaims. "I say, that is a good idea!" The log is big and old but the chums pushing together manage to roll it to the water's edge. Then in it goes and Rupert scrambles onto it to hold it steady.

"Just a minute," Bill says. "We may need this to get back out again so we must make sure it doesn't float away." From his pocket he produces his long fishing line. One end of it he ties to the log, the other he knots around a tree. "Good thinking, Bill" says Rupert. Now Bill joins Rupert on the log. They lie flat and the log begins to drift through the tunnel. The light at the far end gets brighter and then they are back in the sunlight – and the garden.

Almost the first thing that they see –
Their kite stuck halfway up a tree.

Before they can get to their kite
That grumpy old man comes in sight.

The old man's gone so on they push,
But look! A primrose like a bush!

They round a corner. Stop! And stare.
A little girl is standing there.

Almost as soon as they emerge from the tunnel the chums spot their kite. It is caught in the branches of a tree. "Come on, let's get it and get out of here before that old man turns up," urges Bill. They jump ashore and scramble up the bank to the tree. They are almost Rupert when Rupert suddenly grabs Bill's arm and drags him into the bushes. Stomping up a path, looking surlier than ever, comes the grumpy old man. The chums hold their breath.

Luckily for them the old man is too intent on wherever he is going to look in their direction. When they are quite sure he has gone they come out of hiding. They pause to look around. "This is a pretty strange garden," Rupert whispers. "Look at the size of the flowers. This primrose is like a young tree." "I don't think I like this," Bill breathes. "Come on." And so they steal quietly on. Suddenly they stop. Ahead of them a girl is gardening. She turns and stares.

"You two have no right here, you know!
You're trespassing!" she cries. "Now go!"

Then to the chums' dismayed surprise
The little girl breaks down and cries.

"My plants all grow too big and fast,"
She says. "And none of them will last."

As if to prove she doesn't lie
A little tree sweeps Bill up high.

The girl and the chums stare at each other in silence for a moment then the girl cries, "You have no right here! You're trespassing! How dare you!" She seems really upset and the chums have a hard time of it explaining that they mean no harm and that they only want to get their kite back. Suddenly the girl stops being angry. "I am sorry!" she gulps. "But I'm so upset. You see, I'm Mary Quite Contrary and I love my garden but nothing will grow properly." And she weeps.

"Do tell us about it," Rupert begs. "Perhaps we can help." Mary dries her tears and manages a little smile. "That's nice of you," she says. "I don't think you can but . . ." And she explains that her flowers either come up small and withered or quite huge and that the very big ones last no time at all before they wither and die. Just then, as if to prove what she is saying, a small tree behind Bill starts growing so rapidly that it catches his coat and lifts him off his feet.

RUPERT IS INVITED TO STAY

"Hey, get me out of here!" Bill bawls.
The tree is shaken. Down he falls!

"You sneaked in after all, you two?
Just let me get my hands on you!"

"He's our gardener, a lazy one,"
She tells the two chums as they run.

The girl's grandfather says they might,
Because it's so late, stay the night.

Up, up goes the tree with poor Bill struggling helplessly. "Hey, get me down!" he cries. Like an answer to his pleas a large hand emerges from the bushes, grasps the tree's trunk and shakes it hard. Bill lands with a very nasty bump and the others are helping him up when the bushes part and the scowling face of the old man appears. "So you sneaked in after all!" he snarls. "Well, just wait till I lay hands on you." As he starts through the bushes Mary grabs the chums' hands.

"Quick, we must hide," she cries and she drags them off along a maze of paths with the old man lumbering behind. "He's the gardener here," Mary pants. "But he never seems to do any work. My grandfather thinks he is honest and won't get rid of him . . . oh, here is my grandfather." The old gentleman Rupert and Bill are introduced to listens politely to their story of the kite. Of course, they may have it back, he says. But it is late. They must stay the night.

RUPERT STALKS THE GARDENER

They sup and then he shows the pair
The little room that they're to share.

A shadow on the window pane;
The gardener's on the prowl again.

They keep the old man's lamp in sight
And follow him into the night.

They stop. They listen. And they stare.
He's gone into those bushes there.

After a delicious supper Mary's grandfather, who turns out to be a jolly as well as kindly old gentleman, shows Rupert and Bill to their bedroom. It is small but very comfortable. As the pals get ready for bed they talk and they agree that something very odd is going on in Mary's garden. "I'm sure it has something to do with that old gardener," Rupert muses. "He was terribly anxious that no strangers should see inside the garden . . ."

"Sh-sh!" interrupts Bill. "There he goes!" He points to a shadow passing their window. "He's up to no good I'm sure," Rupert whispers. "Come on, let's follow him." Silently, swiftly, the chums slip out of the house. They are in time to see the gardener, clutching a lantern, disappear behind a big tree. On tiptoe they scurry after him. But when they reach the tree there is no sign of him. There is, though, a rustling from a nearby clump of bushes. "He's in there!" breathes Bill.

RUPERT GOES UNDER THE WOODS

They must press on, the two pals see,
If they're to solve the mystery.

Deep in the bushes they have found
Some steep steps that go underground.

They must go on so down they go
And find a weird cave there below.

They find the gardener in that hole
Mixing up powders in a bowl.

The chums stand quite still until the rustling in the bushes stops. "I'm sure the secret is in there somewhere," whispers Rupert. "If we want to discover it we've got to go in." Bill nods and in they plunge. Almost at once they see a bright light in the middle of the clump and make for it. It is coming from a hole in the ground – a hole with steps leading down. The chums exchange looks. They nod and very cautiously Rupert leads the way underground.

What they find at the foot of the steps is the most astonishing sight – a great cavern seemingly full of pillars. The pillars, though, turn out to be the roots of great trees. "We're under the woods," breathes Bill as they pick their way between the roots. Suddenly they freeze in their tracks then duck for cover behind an especially big root. Ahead of them the gardener is standing at a bench covered in bottles and jars. Carefully he is measuring powders into a bowl.

He's done at last and starts to go.
That he's been seen he doesn't know.

"We'll take some samples of this stuff.
Two bottles should be quite enough."

The powder that he made is thrown
Where tiny seedlings have been sown.

A plant that they could barely see
At once shoots up, tall as a tree.

Cowering behind their root Rupert and Bill keep watch on the gardener for what seems a long time. At last he appears to be satisfied with his work. He corks his various bottles and jars then with his bowl starts for the stairs back to the surface. When they are quite sure he has gone the chums leave their hiding-place and approach the bench. "Before we go we better take samples of this," Rupert says. "We may need them." They take two small bottles then set off after the gardener. Back in the garden Rupert and Bill stop for a minute and listen. When they can hear the old gardener moving about they make for the sound. They find him beside one of Mary's flower-beds. As they crouch behind a bush in the darkness they hear him mutter, "This should do the job, heh, heh!" Then he sprinkles some of the powder from his bowl onto a tiny plant. Almost at once the plant shoots to a great height and bursts into bloom. "Now we know!" Rupert whispers.

Then silently they steal away.
They'll tell what they have seen next day.

"This powder," Rupert says, "will show
How all your plants are forced to grow."

He finds a tiny pimpernel
To demonstrate the old man's spell.

They gasp. They can't believe their eyes.
The plant's now an enormous size.

Delighted at having solved the mystery of Mary Contrary's garden, Rupert and Bill hurry back to the house and their beds. First thing next day, they agree, they will tell Mary's grandfather. And so straight after breakfast next morning they go to the old gentleman and pour out their story. Being a very fair as well as a kindly man he can't believe that his old gardener could be up to no good. "Then, please, sir, at least come and see what his powder does," Rupert pleads.

The old man agrees, but not very willingly, and out they go into the garden. In the middle of a path Rupert spies a tiny pimpernel. "This will do," he says. He sprinkles it with some of the powder. In a moment it is a towering bush. "The villain!" cries Mary's grandfather when he has got over his surprise. "Plainly he has invented this powder so that he doesn't have to work at making things grow, even though he knows the poor flowers will die quickly!"

RUPERT GETS HIS KITE BACK

But now they see the tragic plight
Of what grew up so fast last night.

The gardener is shown the door.
"Be off!" he's told. "Return no more."

And so at last the pals are free
To get their kite down from the tree.

"What, this log?" Rupert laughs. "Oh, dear!
That is how Bill and I got here."

Now Rupert leads the way to the plant Bill and he saw grow so rapidly last night. It lies shrivelled on the ground. "Oh, this is too much!" cries Mary's grandfather. "I shall dismiss him at once!" When the gardener is told that his mischief has been discovered he tries at first to bluster and lie but he soon sees that he is wasting his time. "Go!" orders Mary's grandfather. "And remember that a beautiful garden can only be created by hard work and loving care."

With the mystery cleared up and the gardener banished, Rupert and Bill remember what brought them to the garden in the first place – the kite. With the old gentleman's permission Rupert, who is very good at climbing, shins up the tree and gets the kite. Luckily it is quite undamaged. Then something catches the old gentleman's eye. "What is that log doing in our stream?" he asks. "Oh, dear," chuckles Rupert. "That's how Bill and I got in here past the gardener."

The pals are taken to some stairs
And shown a boat they're told is theirs.

But now it's time to leave and so
They say their thanks and off they go.

The trees are dense, the light is dim
As down the little stream they skim.

Something, they feel, is not quite right.
The gardener has them in sight.

"Come with me," says Mary's grandfather with a smile, and leads the way downstream. He stops beside a neat little boat moored at the foot of some steps. "That is your reward for helping me," he says. "I'm sure you will find it a lot more comfortable than a log." Of course, Rupert and Bill want to set off at once to try their new boat but Mary makes them wait until she has made sandwiches to eat on their homeward journey. Then with a last wave the two pals set off.

After the garden the woods seem gloomier and thicker than ever. "I hope we can reach Nutwood by keeping to the stream," says Bill. "I don't fancy leaving the boat and having to go through the woods again." Nor does Rupert and it isn't just because the woods look so uninviting. He has a feeling that they are being watched. And he is right. For tracking them along the bank, dodging from tree to tree, is the old gardener, who is determined to get his own back.

RUPERT IS CAPTURED

At last they reach a sunlit lake
And Rupert says, "Let's have a break."

They find a place that seems just right
And go ashore to have a bite.

They settle down to eat their lunch.
But someone steals up as they munch.

The pals are taken by surprise.
"You're going to pay!" the gardener cries.

Soon after Bill takes a turn at paddling the boat the stream flows out into a broad sunlit lake. "That's a bit better," Rupert says. "I didn't like that stretch through the woods at all." By now the pair are beginning to feel hungry. "Head for that old tower," Rupert says. "We can picnic there." Near the tower they find a flat stretch where they can beach their boat. They take their things out of it, the kite, the paddle and the sandwiches and settle down to rest and eat.

But as they munch and chat about their adventure they little realise that it is not over. For stealing through the bushes behind them comes the gardener who has followed them round the shore. Suddenly when they are least expecting it, he springs. He grabs them by their arms. "Aha!" he snarls. "You didn't think, did you, that I'd let you away with losing me my job like that. No, no, I'm going to make sure you pay for that!"

RUPERT IS PUT TO WORK

He tells the pals, "You'll come with me."
In vain they struggle to break free.

"I make my powders here, and you
Shall have the dirty work to do!"

He locks them in this dismal hole
To carry sacks and shovel coal.

And when at length the man returns,
He has their paddle which he burns.

Rupert and Bill wriggle and squirm but they cannot break free of the gardener's grip and they find themselves being dragged up the overgrown path that leads to the old tower. The gardener bundles them inside then slams and locks the door with a key he takes from his pocket. They don't have to wonder long how he comes to have a key to the tower. "Bad luck you chose to stop near here," he gloats, waving the key at them. "This is the place I make my magic gardening powder."

He grins at the dismay on the pals' faces. "Now you're going to do all the hard part of that work like shovelling coal for the furnace." And hard work it is, both hot and dirty. After a while the gardener goes off somewhere. "We must try to get outside, even if only for a moment," Rupert whispers. "Then we can get away in the boat." But their captor has thought of that too. When he returns he is carrying their paddle. "Just in case . . ." he growls, and puts it in the furnace.

59

They're ordered to a loft to sleep.
So, tired and grimy, up they creep.

Bill pulls a bottle out, says, "Look,
Here's half the growing stuff we took!"

"With luck," he says, "there may well be
Somewhere down there a tiny tree."

But no strong tree springs up, alas!
The only thing that grows is grass.

At last the day draws to a close and the pals are told they can stop work. "You two sleep up in the loft where you can't play any tricks," the gardener tells them and makes them climb to the top of the tower. Rupert is still clutching the kite. "Get a good night's sleep," the old man says, grinning unpleasantly. "You will be working even harder tomorrow." When the man has gone, locking them in, Rupert slumps onto a box looking glum. But Bill seems excited.

From a pocket inside his jacket he produces one of the bottles of the gardener's growing powder they took the night before. "This makes plants grow very fast, doesn't it?" he begins. Rupert nods. Bill crosses to the window and Rupert follows. "So if there's a tiny tree growing under this window . . ." Bill says, sprinkling the powder on the ground below. "It will grow up here and we can climb down it!" Rupert cries. But there is no tree. Just a lot of useless grass.

"Cheer up!" cries Rupert. "I've a plan
By which we might escape that man."

"Bill, hold it steady while I write
A message telling of our plight."

They cut the string. The kite goes free.
And with it goes their rescue plea.

Both pals feel they have done their best
To get away and now can rest.

Poor Bill is terribly upset that his clever plan has come to nothing, especially as he has used almost half the powder. He is so upset that Rupert starts thinking doubly hard about a way to get out of the tower. Then – "I've got it!" he cries. "The kite, of course! We'll write a message on it and let it fly away. Someone is bound to find it and come to our rescue." Bill cheers up at once and holds the kite steady while Rupert writes on the kite with the stub of pencil he always carries in a pocket just in case. Then they carry the kite to the window. Good! The wind is still high. Rupert launches the kite and waits till it is pulling strongly before he cuts the line with the knife he also always carries in his pocket just in case. Away goes the kite high over the trees. Now that there is a chance of someone learning of their plight and coming to help them the pals feel a lot more cheerful and settle down on a bed of straw and sacks.

They sleep right through until it's light.
And look! Outside the tower – the kite!

"Yes, Rollo's trying hard to steer
So we can pull the kite in here."

They reach right out and grab the thing.
Its message says, "Pull in the string".

They haul the string and find their friend
Has tied a stout rope to the end.

"Rupert! Quick, look!" Rupert is wakened from a deep sleep by Bill's urgent cry. His chum is on his feet and pointing excitedly at something outside the window. "The kite!" he gasps. "It's back!" And he leaps up to join Bill at the window. "Bill," he cries, "it's Rollo!" There, some way from the tower is one of their friends, Rollo. Skilfully he is keeping the kite near their window. "I'm sure he wants us to pull it in," Rupert says. "Get ready to grab it when it comes near enough."

A moment later the kite comes into reach. Bill catches hold of it and pulls it inside. "Look!" Rupert says, "He's rubbed out our message and written something in its place . . . 'Pull in the kite string'." They lean out of the window and wave to show that they have understood. The string, when they start to pull it, is surprisingly heavy. They soon see why. Rollo has attached it to a length of sturdy rope which is coiled beside him.

RUPERT AND HIS PALS FLEE

They fix the rope and down they go
To Rollo waiting there below.

He says he found the kite last night
And came as soon as it was light.

The old man's gone out, but he may
Be back soon so they speed away.

Alas, it looks as if they're caught!
He's come back sooner than they thought.

Rupert and Bill pull the end of the rope into the loft and tie it securely to a bolt set in the wall. "Right, down we go," Rupert says. "You first, Bill." Bill swings himself out onto the rope and Rupert follows, but not before he has cut loose their precious kite to bring with him. As they reach the ground Rollo runs up to meet them. "I found your message yesterday evening," he says, "and came round here at first light. I thought you were never going to wake up. That old man went off somewhere very early and as soon as he was out of sight I started flying the kite." "Well, we better be off before he comes back," Rupert urges. "Right!" Rollo says. "Let's make for camp. It's quite near and he will never think of looking there." They set off at a run. "I thought we were never going to escape," Bill pants as they go. "But we have." Bill has spoken too soon. An angry shout! And there is the gardener bearing down on them.

RUPERT FOILS THE GARDENER

Rupert turns and hopes he can
With growing powder stop the man.

It causes him enough delay
To let the three pals get away.

The only route that they can take
Is by their boat across the lake.

"The gardener burnt our paddle so
We'll have to use our hands to row."

The old man has come back sooner than they hoped! For an instant they stare at each other then as the gardener makes a rush at them our three turn and flee. But they are running in the direction of the lake and the gardener is gaining on them. Rupert is aware of something bulky in his pocket that is making running more difficult. It's the bottle with the rest of the growing powder Bill had. He remembers picking it up as he left the tower . . . brainwave!

He stops, uncorks the bottle and scatters its contents on the ground. Almost at once the grass springs up like a jungle, halting their pursuer and giving the chums precious seconds to reach the shore and the boat. Rupert and Bill scramble aboard while Rollo pushes the boat out. As he follows the other two into it the gardener bursts out of the long grass, yelling angrily. "Paddle with your hands, Rollo!" Rupert cries. "That man burnt our paddle to stop us escaping."

Although they've left the man behind,
To row by hand's too hard, they find.

"The answer," Rupert cries, "is clear.
It's with us in the boat, right here!"

Because the wind's still blowing strong
The kite can pull the boat along.

So there is no need for an oar.
They glide towards the distant shore.

The push Rollo gave the boat was a hefty one and carries the three chums far enough from the shore to leave the gardener dancing in helpless rage. And it's as well he did push hard, for although the three paddle furiously with their hands they make sadly little progress and soon they are exhausted. On shore the gardener is still hopping about in the hope the boat without a paddle may drift back towards him. Then Rupert suddenly laughs. "We are silly!" he cries. "We have the answer right here in the boat with us." The other two sit up and stare. "This!" Rupert declares and produces the kite which Bill and he have been careful not to leave behind despite all the excitement. While the others watch he ties the kite's string to the ring in the prow of the boat. Then he launches the kite which at once is picked up by the strong wind. And over the lake it goes towing the boat behind it. "Ah, now, this is the way to travel!" chuckles Rollo.

And now the kite, so it would seem,
Is going to take them up a stream.

"I thought I recognised this brook,"
Rupert exclaims, "There's Nutwood! Look!"

Not many minutes pass before
They moor their boat and jump ashore.

Then Rupert's parents hurry out
To see what this is all about.

As the kite pulls the boat over the lake the pals learn how to steer it. All they need do is trail their hands in the water. And it is as well they can steer when they reach the stream on the far side of the lake with all its twists and turns. All thoughts of going to the gipsy camp have had to be forgotten, but something even safer lies ahead. Quite suddenly Rupert finds that he recognises bushes and trees and stretches of bank. "We're near Nutwood!" he cries. "What a bit of luck! This stream runs right past the bottom of our garden!" And in no time at all they are mooring the little boat just outside Rupert's back garden gate while Mr and Mrs Bear hurry down to see what all the fuss is about. "Where on earth have you been?" Mr Bear wants to know. "Mummy and I have been so worried." "Just wait till I tell you all the exciting things we've been doing!" Rupert says as Podgy, Algy and Willie run to welcome him.

Now Rupert tells how Bill and he
Cleared up the garden mystery.

But Podgy scoffs at what he hears.
"What? Magic powder? No!" he jeers.

Right! Podgy shall see how it grows.
What's left is scattered round his toes.

The last laugh is on Podgy who
Peers out like something in a zoo.

At each turn of Rupert's tale his listeners gasp. All of them, that is, except Podgy Pig who is always too ready to believe that people are making things up; maybe because he makes things up himself sometimes. Whenever Rupert says anything about the magic growing powder Podgy makes a great show of bursting out laughing. "Oh, come on, Rupert!" he guffaws. "You don't expect us to believe that, do you?" At last Rupert has had enough of Podgy's rudeness. He has kept the bottle which contained the magic growing powder because it still has a little left in it. Now he opens it and sprinkles the grains of powder on the ground in front of Podgy. "Here, what are you doing?" Podgy cries. 'What's that stuff you're throwing about . . . I say, what's happening? Look at the grass . . . get me out of here!" For now the grass has sprung up around him and he is peering out of it like something in a zoo. And how the others laugh at his antics! THE END

Rupert's Picture Puzzle

This picture was painted by Alex Cubie for Rupert's Adventure Series. It shows Rupert and his mummy playing a game which you can join in too. Every letter in the alphabet is represented by at least one of the objects in this room. Can you write down what they all are?

RUPERT®

and the
Bearcycle

RUPERT GETS A SURPRISE

"Good morning, Rupert! Close your eyes,"
Says Daddy. "Here's a big surprise!"

"A glider!" Rupert cheers with joy,
He cannot wait to build his toy.

So Daddy reads aloud the guide,
Then says, "Let's build the plane outside."

They build the wings and cockpit, too.
Says Rupert Bear, "It's time we flew!"

It's a sunny, summer morning in Nutwood and Rupert Bear is wondering what he might get up to when his daddy gives a big smile and says, "I have a surprise for you, Rupert!" "For me?" Rupert is very excited. What could the surprise be? His daddy tells him to close his eyes, and when Rupert opens them again, Mr Bear is holding a large parcel. Rupert reads the writing on the front of the parcel. It's a kit for building a glider! "Oh, thank you!" Rupert cries.

Building the glider is a job for two, and Mr Bear is glad to help Rupert. "We'll just sit down and read the guide first . . ." he mutters. Soon they realise that the wingspan will be quite wide once it's finished. "We'd better build your glider outside," says Mr Bear, and so they head out to the garden. Rupert puts the pieces of the cockpit together, and his daddy attaches the wings and propeller. It looks fantastic! "I say, it's ready to fly!" Rupert cheers happily.

RUPERT TRIES HIS GLIDER

They launch the plane towards the sky,
And marvel as it starts to fly.

But with a sudden gust of air,
The plane heads straight for Mrs Bear!

And then the glider swerves around,
And pushes Daddy to the ground!

If Rupert wants another try,
He must go somewhere else to fly.

"Now, launch it carefully . . ." Daddy instructs, but Rupert is so excited that he barely hears what Mr Bear is saying. The glider takes off beautifully at first, as the breeze catches it just right. But then there is a sudden, strong gust of wind, and Rupert's glider banks sharply towards Mrs Bear, who at that very moment is hanging out the washing. "Oh, do look out!" Rupert calls to his mummy, and Mrs Bear looks up and gasps. The glider is flying straight at her!

Mrs Bear ducks just in time, and the glider sails past her. And then the model plane swerves again, and heads straight towards Mr Bear. "Oh my goodness!" Mr Bear shouts as he drops to the ground, to avoid being hit. The plane finally glides down gently and comes to rest in the bushes, but Mr and Mrs Bear are frowning. "Rupert, perhaps you need to take your new toy to Nutwood Common where there's more open space," Mr Bear suggests.

"I'll go to Nutwood Common then,"
Thinks Rupert Bear, "and try again."

"What's that you've got?" His chums are keen
To fly the glider on the green.

The glider takes off on its flight
And reaches a fantastic height!

When Rupert tries to guide it down,
He soon is lifted off the ground!

Rupert agrees that Nutwood Common is a far better place for launching his new glider. He sets off, and once he reaches the Common he spies his chums, who are out to play as well. "Hullo, it's Algy, Bingo, Edward, Podgy and Bill. I can't wait to show them my glider!" Rupert thinks. He calls out to his friends, who all come running over. "What's that you've got there, Rupert?" says Algy Pug. "My daddy and I just finished building this glider!" Rupert replies.

"It's topping!" Bill Badger declares. "Does it fly?" "Yes, it looks quite big . . . does it generate enough lift to oppose its weight?" adds Bingo the Brainy Pup. "Of course it flies!" says Rupert, laughing. "Just you watch!" He launches the glider again and, to his delight, it soars into the sky. "Hurrah!" his chums all cheer. The glider stays adrift for quite some time. After watching it for a while, Rupert reaches up to guide it down . . . only to be lifted clear off the ground!

"Oh come back, Rupert Bear – please wait!"
His chums all cry, but it's too late!

The plane climbs higher in the air,
Still carrying poor Rupert Bear!

He soars along, until the breeze
Propels the plane into the trees.

Still shaking, Rupert stops and blinks.
"What's that? A giant bird?" he thinks.

"Oh, help!" Rupert cries to his friends. His chums chase after him, but to no avail – the little bear is already high up in the sky and out of their reach. "Come back!" they call, but Rupert is too frightened to let go of the glider. The plane climbs higher still, and Rupert sees the houses and trees getting smaller and smaller. "I'll have to wait until the wind changes and the glider drifts back down," he thinks. "Oh, I do hope it's soon – I can't hold on much longer!"

At that very moment, the glider dips down in the sky, and the long wings catch in the thick foliage of a tall oak tree below. The plane shudders to a stop, and Rupert clings to the large branches, shaken but unhurt. "Phew, that was quite a ride!" he says to himself. "It will be all right, now – I just need to climb down from this tree and find my way back home." As if in response, he hears a loud squawk. He turns around quickly. Behind him, there is a giant bird!

RUPERT MEETS THE SQUIRREL KING

As Rupert turns to look about,
A friendly squirrel scampers out.

"We have to feed the chick, you see –
We don't know where his mum might be!"

"Please come with us," the squirrels sing,
"It's time for you to meet our King!"

The King of Squirrels, wise and fair,
Has just the quest for Rupert Bear.

"Hello, is this your tree?" Rupert says to the bird, politely. "I'm terribly sorry to have crashed into it." "No, it's *our* tree!" calls a muffled voice that sounds like it's coming from inside the tree. Rupert peers up and sees a red squirrel clambering out from a small door in the tree trunk. "This tree belongs to the Squirrel King, but we're looking after the jay – he's just a baby, you see. Why don't you come inside with me, and I'll explain everything there?"

Rupert nods, and crawls inside the tree after the squirrel, who makes a chattering noise. All of a sudden, four more squirrels scamper up to greet them. "Watch your step, there's a ladder to climb down . . ." they chatter to Rupert. "Come down here with us, and you can meet our king!" Rupert is still wondering why the squirrels are looking after the jay chick, but then he sees a handsome squirrel wearing a shiny crown. This must be the Squirrel King!

RUPERT SETS OFF FOR THE SEA

The King explains, "That hungry jay –
His mum was taken far away."

"I'll rescue her! At least, I'll try,"
Says Rupert, as he says goodbye.

So Rupert sets off on his way,
Still hoping he can save the day.

But soon he stops. He doesn't know
In which direction he should go.

The other squirrels stop chattering, and the Squirrel King begins to speak. "The poor chick's mother was captured by trappers two days ago," he explains to Rupert. "We've been feeding him as well as we can, but he's such a large jay that soon our stash of acorns will run out. We cannot leave our tree, so we need someone to go out and rescue his mother." Rupert agrees to try to help. "Do you know where the trappers might be?" Rupert asks them.

The Squirrel King explains that the trappers were heading south, towards the sea. "This door will lead you out of our tree and onto the path," he says, "and we'll bring your glider down for you." Two squirrels scamper up to retrieve the glider, which is bent at the front, but still in one piece and able to fly. Rupert waves goodbye to the squirrels and starts off along the path towards the sea. After a little while, he comes to a crossroads and isn't sure which way to go.

RUPERT MEETS THE BEARCYCLE

Then Rupert spies a tiny shop,
And guesses he should make a stop.

The owner deals in bike repair.
He warmly greets the little bear.

So Rupert Bear explains his quest,
To bring the bird back to her nest.

The Bearcycle has found a clue –
A giant feather, brown and blue!

"Let me see . . . which way is south?" Rupert mutters to himself as he looks about for a clue. But he can't tell, so he heads in the direction of a small shop off in the distance. "I'll ask for directions," he decides, "and maybe they'll know something about the mother jay!" The shop looks open, so Rupert pushes the door. Inside, he can see bicycles on the floor and bicycles on the walls – it must be a bicycle repair shop! "Hello, there!" a friendly voice greets him from behind the counter.

"Just call me the Bearcycle!" the large bear adds with a chuckle. "Now, how can I help you?" Rupert introduces himself and explains about his journey. "I'm trying to rescue a captured bird. I think she was taken south, towards the sea," Rupert says. The Bearcycle thinks for a moment, then asks, "A *giant* jay?" "Yes, how did you know?" Rupert replies in surprise. The Bearcycle takes Rupert outside to show him what he found – it's a giant feather!

RUPERT MAKES A NEW FRIEND

"A truck came rumbling past my store,
And dropped the feather near the door."

"Hurrah!" cheers Rupert Bear. "What luck,
The bird must be inside the truck!"

The Bearcycle says, "Come with me,
We'll ride together to the sea."

So off they go, and as they ride,
They spot more feathers on the side.

The Bearcycle tells Rupert everything he knows. "Two nights ago, a truck passed by my shop around midnight. I did think that there was something suspicious about someone driving past so late at night. When I went outside in the morning, I found this feather on the ground." "That's it!" Rupert exclaims. "The trappers must have captured the mother jay when it was dark, and then hidden her inside their truck. I must hurry if I want to catch them."

"You'll be much faster if I come along," the Bearcycle says. "We can ride together! I'll go and find the right bicycle for us." Rupert is very happy to accept the Bearcycle's offer. He decides to leave his glider at the shop, and he props it up behind the counter. "All aboard!" the Bearcycle calls. Rupert climbs onto his shoulders, and they're off! As the Bearcycle pedals on, Rupert looks down and sees another feather on the path. "We must be on the right track!" he cheers.

They're nearly at the pathway's end,
When Rupert spots another friend.

It's Sailor Sam! And once he's heard,
Their tale, he's fearful for the bird.

Says Sam, "I'll help you if I can."
And Rupert thinks, "I have a plan."

The path is wet; the little bear
Must climb down all the rocks with care.

Soon, Rupert hears the cries of seagulls and smells salt in the air. "We must be near the ocean now," he thinks. Then the sea comes into view, and Rupert spies something else. At the shore stands a familiar-looking man. "Why, it's my old friend, Sailor Sam!" Rupert calls out in surprise. Rupert starts to wave, and after a moment Sam waves back, once he recognises the little bear. "Hullo there, Rupert! What brings you down to the sea?"

Rupert explains to Sam why they've come this way, and introduces him to his new friend, the Bearcycle. Sam looks worried when he hears their story. "Yes, I've seen some men near the caves down by the cliff, but it's a dangerous climb." "Oh dear, but we have to rescue the mother jay!" Rupert says. "I'll be quiet so the trappers don't hear me coming." "Then I'm coming too," says Sailor Sam. "Yes, and I will join you as well," says the Bearcycle.

RUPERT HEADS INTO THE CAVE

"We must keep very cool and brave,"
Says Rupert, peering in the cave.

As Rupert tiptoes down the hall,
He spies a large jay – five feet tall.

"We've all come here to set you free,"
Says Rupert, reassuringly.

Then suddenly, they hear a screech –
The crooks returning to the beach!

Rupert takes the lead, and the other two follow him further down the rocks and into the mouth of the cave. The entrance is concealed behind a jagged rock, and Rupert sees that it would make a very good hiding place. Inside the cave, Rupert has a look around and decides that the trappers must be out, because the cave is empty. Well, not *quite* empty – Rupert spies a giant crate in the corner, with a fluffy wing poking out. It must be the mother jay!

Rupert tiptoes carefully up to the jay so as not to alarm her, and whispers, "Don't worry, we're friends – we're here to rescue you!" The jay cocks her head and looks back at Rupert, so the little bear knows that she understands him. "Oh dear, there's another crate at the back!" whispers the Bearcycle. "It looks like the trappers have captured some other birds too!" Suddenly, they hear voices coming in from the beach. The trappers must be returning to the cave!

"The smugglers!" Rupert gasps. "Oh, dear,
We're finished if they find us here!"

"We'll hide now," Sam calls to his mates.
"Let's crouch behind the giant crates."

The bird blinks twice, then gives a yelp,
As if to say, "Oh, let me help!"

When Rupert opens up the crate,
The large bird doesn't hesitate.

"What will we do?" Rupert worries. "We don't have time to climb back out, but the trappers won't be happy if they find us here!" "Shh," whispers Sam. "We'll have to hide and be as quiet as we can." The crate is large enough for both Rupert and Sam to crouch behind it. The trappers come closer, and Rupert hears what they're saying. They're going to sell the giant jay to someone who will take her far, far away. "We can't let that happen!" Rupert thinks.

The jay leans towards Rupert and pokes him gently with her beak. "I think she wants us to open the crate and let her out, but it's locked!" Rupert whispers to Sam. "Look!" Sam replies. "The plank near the top is loose. Do you think you can wiggle it free?" Rupert tries nudging the plank up, then down. "Hullo! So it *is* loose! I think I might be able to slide it out . . ." The whole side soon comes apart, and Rupert removes the top. The jay is free!

She soars up high, then squawks with glee,
And knocks the crooks into the sea!

The friends all laugh, then go around
Releasing other birds they've found.

"Your chick is safe and sound, it's true,"
Says Rupert, "But she misses you!"

The large jay flaps her wings with flair,
As if to thank the little bear.

The jay soars gracefully into the air. She opens her beak and screeches angrily at the trappers, who are so scared that they dash back to their boat. But the jay is still flying straight towards them! With a mighty swoop, she knocks the trappers right off the side of their boat, and they fall into the ocean. Meanwhile, the Bearcycle has used his bicycle repair kit to open all of the other crates, and Rupert cheers as another flock of birds fly free!

The large jay flies back over to Rupert, and bows her head low, as if to say thank you to the little bear. "Your baby chick is fine," Rupert reassures her, smiling. "The squirrels are looking after him for you, although I know he misses you very much!" The jay raises her left wing and gives it a wave, then takes off into the sky. "Goodbye!" Rupert calls, as he watches her set off back home. "Oh, what an afternoon it's been!" laughs Sam as he watches the bird disappear.

"It's time for us to go home, too,"
Says Sailor Sam. "I'll ride with you."

The Bearcycle comes passing by.
He's fixed the plane – it's safe to fly!

When he wakes up the next clear day,
The bear invites his friends to play.

Let's launch our planes now – three, two, one –
And go!" calls Rupert Bear. "What fun!"

"Yes, and I must be getting home," Rupert says. Sam offers to drive him back, and the Bearcycle promises to stop by later. "And I'll bring a surprise . . ." he says, smiling mysteriously. Later that day, after Rupert has returned home and told his parents all about his adventure, there is a knock on the door. It's the Bearcycle again, and he's holding Rupert's glider! "I've fixed this for you," the Bearcycle smiles. "Now it will fly exactly where you want it to!"

Since his glider is fixed now, Mr and Mrs Bear don't mind if Rupert plays with it in the garden. "Oh, please may I invite my chums round to play with it, too?" Rupert asks, and his parents agree. Rupert's chums arrive with planes of their own, so they can all launch them together. Soon, the air is filled with planes of all sizes whizzing back and forth and narrowly missing each other. "What fun!" calls Rupert Bear. "And what an adventure today has been!" THE END

Spot the Difference

It's a windy day and Rupert and his pals are having lots of fun in the garden.
There are 8 differences between the two pictures. Can you spot them all?

RUPERT and the

Rupert has climbed up to the crest
And near the old mill stops to rest.

It is the sort of crisp, sunny morning Rupert loves. There is no school today and he has gone exploring on the ridge behind Nutwood. When he stops to catch his breath after a steep climb he sees that he is near the old windmill. It hasn't been used for years, not since the miller built a bigger mill nearer the village. And that is why Rupert jumps up in amazement when suddenly the mill's sails start to turn.

WINDMILL

But look! The sails are racing round.
It seems the mill might leave the ground.

What's happening? What's this about?
Rupert runs over to find out.

Rupert stares. The mill is bouncing up and down on the post that runs up the middle of it. "It's not supposed to be able to work!" Rupert gasps as the old structure bounces as if it were about to take off. "Oh, I must see what this is all about!" And off he dashes along the ridge to where the mill is rocking and swaying as its sails turn ever faster. Then as he runs up the slope towards the mill it stops.

He soon gets to it but by then
The mill's its old still self again.

John Harrold

RUPERT TELLS HIS PALS

"Is anyone in there?" he cries.
The door stays shut. No one replies.

There's something here that is not right.
He feels someone has him in sight.

His chums look up at Rupert's yell
And wonder what he has to tell.

The windmill doesn't move a bit.
The chums think he imagined it.

The mill is so quiet again that for a moment Rupert wonders if he really did see it moving. "Of course, I did," he says aloud. "And since it couldn't start by itself someone must be inside it." He stares up at it. "Hello!" he shouts. "Anyone there?" The only answer is the sighing of the wind. Uneasily Rupert climbs to the mill door and calls again. No answer. The door is locked. But as he turns away he feels that someone in the windmill is watching him.

On Nutwood common Bill Badger, Algy Pug and Willie Mouse are playing football. But they stop when Rupert runs up and blurts out his story about the mill. "I'm sure someone's in there," he ends. "The wind must have made the sails start up," Bill says. And Willie adds, "Maybe you just imagined someone in there." "Then why don't we go and have a look," Algy suggests. So some time later the pals arrive at the mill. It looks exactly as usual.

Says Willie, "It won't move, I fear
While all of us are standing here."

They all agree with Willie so
The four of them pretend to go.

Pretending not to care they stride
Away then find a place to hide.

They wait what seems like ages then
The mill begins to move again.

Cautiously the four pals approach the windmill. They circle it slowly looking for anything at all unusual. Algy is the first to speak. "It looks the way it's looked for ages," he says. Bill and he look at Rupert as if they feel he may have been pulling their legs. "Oh, I did see it moving!" protests Rupert who can see what they are thinking. Then Willie pipes up, "Maybe it won't do anything while we're all standing here. Let's pretend to go away."

So off tramp the pals trying to look as if windmills were the last things in their minds. But as soon as they reach a bushy hollow they stop and hide. As they crouch there Willie whispers to Rupert, "A moment ago I felt the way you did, that someone was watching me from the mill." For a long time nothing happens then just when they are thinking of giving up Bill cries, "Look, it's working again, Rupert, just the way you said it did!"

RUPERT IS PROVED RIGHT

The mill begins to bounce and dance.
"Hurry!" cries Rupert. "Now's our chance."

Then when they're almost at the top
The mill slows down. It's going to stop.

"So there," says Rupert, "Now you know
That what I said I saw was so."

The other chums swing round and stare
As Willie cries, "There's someone there!"

The pals gape as the sails of the windmill spin faster and faster and the building bounces up and down on its post. "Come on!" Rupert cries, and jumps to his feet. And off he dashes to the mill with the others close behind. "I say, it's going to take off!" gasps Bill as for a moment the mill bounces quite clear of its post. But it settles back again and by the time the chums reach the crest of the ridge where it stands it has almost stopped once more. But now they have all seen it working.

"There! You see I was right!" crows Rupert. And all four of them go round the mill calling out things like, "We know you're in there!" and "Why don't you open up?" and "Who are you?" Then Willie who has started up the steps to the door squeaks, "Look! There's someone at the window!" The others dash to the little mouse and stare up at where he is pointing. Behind a grimy window a shape of someone-or something-can be seen.

Rupert and the Windmill
RUPERT IS INVITED INSIDE

They all gaze up. A window creaks.
"Oh, look, it's Bingo!" Willie squeaks.

"Oh, well, " says Bingo, "now I'm found
You lot may just as well look round."

"I've done my best, I should explain,
To make this old mill work again."

The whole thing really has been fun,
Though quite a lot still must be done.

The pals hold their breath. All eyes are on the window. It creaks open . . . "Bingo!" Rupert and the others shout as their chum Bingo, the clever pup, sticks his head out. "I might have known you lot wouldn't give up as easily once you got curious," he chuckles. "What's it all about?" "What are you up to?" the questions tumble out from the pals. "Hey, just a second!" pleads Bingo and disappears to emerge a moment later at the door. "You'd better come in and have a look," he says. Agog, the others follow Bingo into the mill. "It has been standing here doing nothing for ages," Bingo explains, "so I decided to see if I could get it going again. As you can see I've got the sails working." "What's this?" asks Algy, examining a stout pillar in the middle of the floor. "That's the post the mill turns on," Bingo says. "It seems a bit loose on its post," remarks Rupert. "Yes, I'll fix it," Bingo says leading the way upstairs.

89

"What's this?" A rope's caught Willie's eye.
He doesn't wait for a reply.

"Hey, don't touch that for any sake!"
Cries Bingo. "That controls the brake."

Now Willie has released the brake
The mill begins to groan and shake.

Bingo leaps up in frantic hope
To stop the sails. He snaps the rope.

They stop in a room full of the mill's old machinery. "You know, the mill almost took off while we were watching it," Rupert says. "Yes, that's because I still have to fix the post and this thing that stops the sails turning too fast," Bingo replies. He points to a chain hanging from the ceiling. He is just about to explain how it works when Willie squeaks, "What's this?" and unhitches a rope from the wall. "No, don't!" Bingo yells. "That's the brake!" But too late.

Willie has let go of the rope. At the same moment there comes a great groaning and whirring. The mill begins to shake so much that the pals can hardly stand. "The sails have started to turn again!" Bingo cries as he tugs on the brake rope. "Give me a hand, quick!" But before Rupert can cross the heaving floor Bingo gives a cry and falls flat on his back. The brake rope has snapped. And now the sails are turning faster and faster.

"This brake-rope thing I must repair!"
Cries Bingo, rushing for the stair.

Then, sudden as a thunderbolt,
The windmill gives a mighty jolt.

How strange! Although the shaking ends,
The shaft still turns, observe the friends.

Now Rupert crosses to look out.
"Oh, no!" He gives a frightened shout.

The pals stare at each other in dismay as the mill judders and shakes and the squeal of the turning sails grows faster and louder. Rupert can feel the floor beginning to pitch and sway. Bingo manages to scramble to his feet. He gathers the brake rope and starts for the stairs. "I must try to fix this rope to the brake again," he cries. "Come on, Rupert. Give me a hand!" Rupert is about to follow when the mill gives a mighty lurch, throwing everyone flat.

For what seems ages the mill shakes and heaves and creaks and groans while the chums sprawl helplessly on the floor. Then just as suddenly all the movement stops. For a moment the pals are too surprised to speak. They pick themselves up. "The sails must have stopped," Algy suggests. "No, they haven't!" Bingo cries and points to the shaft joining the sails to the grindstones. It is still spinning fast. Then Rupert, who has gone to the window, cries "Oh, no!"

The others quickly gather round.
The windmill's far above the ground.

The huge sails drive it through the air.
It's going fast – but going where?

Says Bingo, "If the sails don't slow
Then right on flying we shall go."

And now the windmill, flying free,
Goes racing out above the sea.

At Rupert's cry of horror the others rush over to the window and crowd round him. For a moment they are silent, unable to believe their eyes. Then Willie squeaks, "Oh, what have I done?" And it is no wonder the pals are horrified. The mill has jumped clear of its post and the Nutwood countryside is rushing past far below. The mill is flying! With the high wind driving its great sails it flies on and on. But going where? In fact, it is going so fast that soon the pals can't recognise the countryside below. Trying hard to sound brave, Rupert asks Bingo, "Which way do you think we're going?" Bingo shakes his head. "I've no idea," he admits. "But this I do know – we won't come down until the wind drops or we can slow the sails. And since we can't do anything about the wind I'm going to have another go at fixing the brake rope." He makes for the stairs but stops and turns when Rupert gasps, "Oh, Bingo, we're over the sea!"

RUPERT HELPS BINGO

"There's just one course for us to take,"
Says Bingo. "First, let's mend the brake."

They can go down. But will they float?
They have to find a ship or boat.

"We've got to keep a look-out and
Find a vessel near which to land."

Bill at the window cries, "I say,
Here comes a ship heading this way!"

This is awful. Flying in a windmill is bad enough. But flying over the sea in one! Then Bingo speaks up: "We must try to slow the mill so that we don't get blown too far out to sea," he says, and once more makes for the stairs. "Rupert, come and give me a hand to repair the sails brake," he calls. Rupert follows and it is while he is helping Bingo that he asks, "Are we going to stop the sails and land on the sea?" "That would be too risky," Bingo says. "We must keep a look-out for a ship." A moment later while Bingo takes a last look at the brake rope Rupert tells the others what has to be done: "Now the brake is mended we can slow the sails and even come down on the sea. But we must land near a ship or we'll be in worse trouble than ever. So everyone keep a sharp look-out for a ship." At that moment Bill who is at the window cries, "Why, there's a ship now!" Sure enough, a fast-looking vessel is making their way.

RUPERT GIVES A WARNING

"Look!" Algy cries. "Now there are two."
But Rupert thinks the first will do.

The sails are slowed. The mill descends.
Then – "Look out, Bingo!" cry his friends.

Just too late Bingo heeds the shout.
A crunch! The pals race to look out.

Two men storm out with angry threat.
Oh, dear. They do seem quite upset.

As the pals crowd to the window to see the ship Algy cries, "Look, there's another ship behind it." "It looks almost as if it's chasing the first one," pipes up Willie. "We better try to bring the mill down near the first one," Rupert says. "It will be under us in a moment." "Then shout when it's almost there," Bingo orders and clutches the brake rope. They hold their breath. "Now!" shouts Rupert. The sails slow as Bingo tugs the rope. The mill sinks gently. "Look out!" Rupert yells. "Let go, Bingo!" Too late. There is an awful crunch and a jolt that sends the pals sprawling. Then silence. The pals pick themselves up. Rupert and Bill are first to the window. "No!" Bill groans. "Oh, no!" repeat the others when they look out. The Windmill has come down slap bang in the middle of the ship's deck as neatly as if it had been built there. Nothing seems to be badly damaged. But from the ship's wheelhouse two men jump down. And they do look angry.

The men turn back. The five pals hear
One say the Customs boat's too near.

"If they are scared of Customs men
Those sailors there are smugglers then!"

The smugglers' boat begins to race
Towards their secret hiding place.

And even with the mill, they find,
They leave the Customs boat behind.

"Oh, dear, what do you think they're going to do?" quavers Rupert staring at the men. Whatever it is, it plainly isn't going to be pleasant for the pals. But suddenly one of the men stops and calls after the other, "We mustn't waste time on them youngsters. We can still get away from the Customs boat. It ain't far to our secret cove." And with that they scramble back into the wheelhouse. "Did you hear that?" breathes Rupert. "If they're running away from a Customs boat they must be smugglers!" The pals stare at each other in dismay. To have landed on of all things a smuggler's boat! Then the boat's engines give a great roar and the windmill sways as the craft surges towards the coast. "Maybe the Customs boat will catch them and save us," Willie says in a trembly voice. They look out at the pursuing Customs boat. It is moving fast. But not fast enough. "It will never catch up in time," Bill whispers to Rupert.

They won't be rescued now, they fear.
Then Rupert has a bright idea.

The others are quite startled when
Rupert lets go the brake again.

Once more the sails are spinning free
And drag the boat back out to sea.

Rupert's delight turns to alarm.
It's plain the smugglers mean them harm.

The coast – and the smugglers' secret cove – get nearer and nearer as the powerful craft with the windmill on board cuts through the waves. Glumly the chums watch the Customs boat drop further and further behind. "It's hopeless," groans Algy. "This boat's just too powerful." Willie wrings his hands and wails, "What's going to happen to us when they get us ashore?" But Rupert says nothing. He is thinking hard. Suddenly his face lights up and he darts over to the brake rope for the mill's sails. "Hey, what are you up to?" Bingo cries as Rupert unhitches it and the sails begin to creak into action. "Don't you see?" Rupert laughs. "The wind blew the windmill out to sea . . ." "And it will blow us and this boat out to sea again too?" Bingo finishes for him. They feel the vessel slow, stop and then start moving backwards. At the same moment from the deck come screams of rage from two angry smugglers.

RUPERT'S LOT ARE SAVED

They rush to shoot the bolt before
The smugglers reach the windmill door.

"We'll break the door down!" yell the men.
The Customs boat roars up just then.

The chums are asked if they'll make clear
Just what a windmill's doing here.

So Rupert tells the Customs man,
"Well, sir, here's how it all began . . ."

Plainly the smugglers mean to break into the windmill and stop the sails. "Downstairs and bolt the door!" Bingo shouts. The pals scramble below and shoot home the bolts a second before the door shakes under the weight of the two men. Then comes another thump. This time from outside. Looking out, the chums see what made it. The Customs boat has bumped alongside and sailors are jumping aboard. "We give up!" they hear the smugglers shout. Then the pals open the door and step out. "Bless my soul!" gasps the Customs officer. "You don't look smugglers." "Oh, please, we're not!" pipes Willie. "We helped to catch them." The man laughs and soon, with the pals aboard and the smugglers' boat and Windmill in tow, the Customs boat heads for home. "Now," says the officer, "perhaps you'll explain what a windmill's doing here." "Well, sir," Rupert begins, "it all began because there was no school and I went exploring . . ." THE END

RUPERT and

One morning, Rupert wakes to find
Ice patterns Jack Frost's left behind.

One winter morning, Rupert wakes up to find
icy patterns all over his bedroom window . . .
"Jack Frost must have been here!" he laughs. "He
draws on everyone's windows when winter starts!"
The patterns are so pretty that Rupert calls for his
mother to come and see. "How lovely!" she smiles.
"The sun makes them sparkle like diamonds!"
Rupert wonders if Jack is still in Nutwood. Perhaps
he'd let *me* draw patterns too?"

the Deep Freeze

"How beautiful!" smiles Mrs Bear.
"They must mean Winter's in the air!"

"I'll look for Jack! Perhaps he'll know
W'hen Nutwood's due to have some snow . . ."

As soon as he has finished breakfast, Rupert puts on his scarf and hurries outside. It is a crisp, sunny morning but very cold . . . "We must be due for snow soon!" he thinks. "I wonder if Jack knows when?" There is no sign of anyone in the village, so Rupert decides to look for his friend on Nutwood common. Jack Frost normally stays out of sight as he goes about his business but Rupert finally spots him, standing all alone . . .

"There's Jack Frost now! But what's he found?
It looks like something on the ground . . ."

RUPERT MEETS JACK FROST

Then Rupert realises he
Has lost something. "What can it be?"

"My ice thermometer!" says Jack.
"For freezing things! I need it back!"

"I'll help you search," says Rupert. "For
It must be somewhere here – I'm sure!"

No matter how hard Rupert tries
He finds no sign. "It's gone!" he sighs.

To Rupert's surprise, Jack Frost seems to be searching for something. "Hello!" he calls and hurries to join him. "Who's there?" says Jack. "Oh, Rupert! I was so busy I didn't hear you coming . . ." "What have you lost?" asks Rupert. "My thermometer!" sighs Jack. "I'll be in trouble unless I find it!" "We've got one," says Rupert. "Not like mine," says Jack. "It freezes everything it touches. I use it to draw on window panes. My father gave it to me as a special present!"

Rupert offers to help search for the missing thermometer. "It looks like an icicle," Jack tells him. "Be careful not to touch the tip, or else it will freeze you too!" The pair split up, with Rupert combing the common while Jack covers the rest of Nutwood . . . "I can't see any icicle!" thinks Rupert. "Perhaps it's fallen into one of these bushes or got buried in a clump of grass?" The longer Rupert searches, the harder it seems. "Like looking for a needle in a haystack!" he sighs.

RUPERT FINDS A FROZEN POND

Then someone calls out Rupert's name.
"Hey! Come and join our sliding game!"

"A frozen pond!" he blinks. "What fun!
It's big enough for everyone . . ."

The pals walk home and Rupert sees
The fountain's not begun to freeze.

His parents think it's strange the way
That only one pond froze today . . .

Rupert is still looking for Jack Frost's thermometer when he hears the sound of laughter. "It's Podgy and the others!" he smiles. "They're sliding on a frozen pond!" Hurrying to join his chums, he hears how the Fox brothers found the pond and couldn't resist trying it out. "Why don't you have a go?" calls Freddy. "The ice is so thick, it's quite safe!" Rupert takes a run up, then goes whizzing after the others. "Hurrah!" he cries as they slither and slide, over and over again . . .

At last the chums have had enough of their game and everyone makes their way back to Nutwood. "It's odd that nothing else is frozen!" thinks Rupert. "The village fountain normally stops as soon as the weather turns icy but it's flowing as fast as ever . . ." Rupert's parents are surprised to hear about the frozen pond as well. "How odd!" says Mrs. Bear. "Perhaps a freak wind chilled the pond!" "That must be it!" nods Rupert's father. "The barometer said we'd have sunshine . . ."

RUPERT IS MYSTIFIED

Next morning, Mr Bear finds more
Ice patterns - different from before . . .

"A funny drawing!" Rupert blinks.
"That can't be Jack Frost's work!" he thinks.

His mother gives a startled cry.
"My washing's like a board!" But why?

"It must have frozen in the night."
"My word!" gasps Mr Bear, "you're right!"

Next morning, Rupert comes downstairs to find a new set of icy patterns on the window panes. "They look different today!" says Mr Bear. "The ones in the kitchen were more like scribble than pretty flowers . . ." Peering outside, he gives a gasp of surprise, then calls Rupert over to see. "I don't believe it!" he tuts. "It must be one of your chums!" Rupert peers at the drawing. "That doesn't look like one of Jack Frost's drawings!" he says. "But who else could have made it?"

When breakfast is over, Rupert and his parents find more surprises out in the garden . . . "Come and look at my washing!" cries Mrs Bear. "It's frozen stiff!" "Impossible!" says Rupert's father. "The lawn isn't even white . . ." Unpegging a shirt from the line, he holds it up, then shakes his head in disbelief. "Are you sure you didn't use too much starch?" he blinks. "No!" says Mrs Bear. "It's all cold and icy. We must have had a sudden frost overnight."

RUPERT SLIPS ON THE ICE

The High Street's frozen too, it seems.
The icy pavement glints and gleams . . .

"Help!" Rupert cries. He stops his fall
By clutching at a nearby wall!

A lorry's slipped as well. Its load
Is scattered all across the road!

Then Rupert stops, amazed at how
The village fountain's frozen now.

Leaving his parents to puzzle over the frozen washing, Rupert sets off towards the High Street in search of his chums. He hasn't gone far, when he sees a crowd of people gathered together by the side of the road. Hurrying towards them, he finds the pavement is covered in a fine layer of slippery ice. "There must have been a frost after all!" he gasps. "I wonder why it seems so patchy?" Clutching the top of the wall, he sets off again, to see why everyone is staring . . .

When Rupert reaches the High Street, the crowd is so large that he has to push forward to see what is causing the commotion. A lorry has skidded on a patch of ice and shed its load! Parcels and packages lie in a jumbled heap as P.C. Growler tries to clear the way. "It's lucky no-one was hurt!" says Mrs Badger. "Yes!" nods the Professor. "I'm amazed everywhere's so icy! Just look at the village fountain . . ." To Rupert's astonishment, it is completely covered in ice!

The Fox twins shuffle past the throng.
A bandaged Ferdy limps along . . .

"The fountain froze so fast he fell
And dropped the magic wand as well!"

"Wand?" Rupert asks. The twins admit
They drew on window panes with it . . .

There, in the fountain, Rupert sees
Jack's missing wand that makes things freeze!

Rupert is still marvelling at the fountain when he spots the Fox brothers coming out of Dr Lion's surgery. Poor Ferdy has his foot bandaged up and is hobbling along with a stick. "What's happened?" asks Rupert. "Did you slip on the ice?" "That's right," says Freddy. "It froze so quickly we were taken by surprise." "Goodness!" blinks Rupert. "I've never heard of ice freezing that fast before. Where did you fall?" "From the fountain!" says Ferdy. "I slid off and dropped the magic wand!"

"Magic wand?" asks Rupert. "Yes," says Ferdy. "We found it up on the common . . ." "Jack Frost's thermometer!" Rupert cries. "He uses it to draw patterns on everyone's windows." "We tried that!" admits Freddy. "Then we found we could freeze things as well!" Leading Rupert to the fountain's edge, he points down at a glowing light. "*That's* what's making everything icy!" he explains. "The water froze so quickly we couldn't get it back. Now the ice is spreading, all over Nutwood!"

RUPERT TELLS THE PROFESSOR

"Hello!" the old Professor cries.
"This ice is rather a surprise!"

Rupert explains he knows what's made
The ice. "It's trapped here, I'm afraid!"

The Professor tells Bodkin they
Will need a blow-lamp straightaway.

"We need to melt the ice before
This magic wand makes any more!"

As Rupert and Freddy peer down into the ice, they are joined by the Professor, who has come to take a closer look at the fountain. "Fascinating!" he declares. "Everything seems to have frozen so fast!" "Perhaps!" gulps Freddy. "Can't think why! I'd better be off now, Rupert. Got to help Ferdy get home . . ." Without mentioning the Foxes, Rupert tells the Professor how Jack Frost's thermometer is frozen inside the fountain. "That's why Nutwood has suddenly grown so cold!"

While most people would be astonished by Rupert's story, the Professor simply nods his head. "Of course! If the thermometer makes things cold, then ice will go on forming until it's taken out of the fountain . . ." He thinks for a moment, then sends Bodkin to his workshop to fetch a blow-lamp. "Thawing the ice is our only hope," he explains as his servant comes hurrying back. "Chipping it away would take far too long. If something's not done soon, the whole village will be iced-up . . ."

RUPERT IS DISAPPOINTED

The blow-lamp starts to thaw the ice.
"We'll have the wand free in a trice!"

To everyone's dismay they see
The ice re-forming instantly!

Next morning ice is everywhere.
"It's freezing cold!" says Mrs Bear.

The fountain's disappeared from sight
Beneath an icy mound of white.

Bodkin points the blow-lamp at the frozen fountain. "It's melting!" smiles Rupert. "The moment he's finished, I'll reach in and grab Jack's thermometer . . ." Soon Bodkin pushes back his goggles and turns off the lamp. "That's better!" he declares, but, to Rupert's dismay, the water freezes over. "Try again!" orders the Professor, but it's no use. Each time the ice melts, it freezes straightaway. "What a dilemma!" he sighs. "We'll have to think of something else . . ."

Next morning, the ice from the fountain has spread so far it covers the whole village . . . "You'll need to wrap up warm!" says Mrs Bear as she hands Rupert his coat. "Be careful not to slip, dear. The path looks like a skating rink!" As he sets off along the High Street, there are icicles hanging from every window and the fountain has vanished under a frozen mound. "The Professor's here already!" he smiles as he spots his old friend, standing by the fountain, lost in thought . . .

RUPERT FLIES NORTH

The old Professor can't think how
To stop the ice from spreading now . . .

At last the friends agree to go
And visit Jack Frost. "He might know!"

"We're flying North, across the sea.
Rupert can navigate for me . . ."

The pair take off and quickly find
They've left the English coast behind.

The Professor stares at the fountain and shakes his head. "It's no use!" he declares. "Each time we melt the ice it's sure to freeze again . . ." "Jack Frost's thermometer's causing the trouble," says Rupert. "If we told him what's happened, he might know how to stop it!" "Good idea!" nods the Professor. "He lives at the North Pole, doesn't he?" "That's right," says Rupert. "His father has a palace made of ice." "Come on!" says the Professor. "We'll fly there, straightaway . . ."

As soon as the pair reach the Professor's tower, he leads the way to his latest aircraft. "There's only room for two of us," he tells Bodkin. "You stay here, while Rupert helps me navigate." The little servant fills the plane's fuel tank and helps Rupert clamber into the cockpit. The Professor starts the engine and soon they are soaring high over Nutwood, off towards the coast. "I'll keep flying North towards the Pole!" calls the Professor. "Tell me when you spot the palace . . ."

Icebergs and jagged peaks appear.
"The North Pole must be getting near . . ."

A sudden snowstorm starts to blow –
The pair can't see which way to go!

"Who knows how long this storm might last?
We'll have to land until it's passed . . ."

"We'll wait until the snow stops, then
I'll try to find the Pole again!"

For a long time all that Rupert can see is the blue of the ocean down below. At last he spots the jagged peaks of distant mountains and massive icebergs. "This is the start of the Polar ice!" says the Professor. "We shouldn't have much further to go . . ." As he speaks, a dark cloud looms on the horizon, growing larger and larger, until it fills the whole sky. "A snowstorm!" gasps Rupert as icy winds buffet the little plane. "We'll have to land!" calls the Professor. "I can't see where I'm going!"

By the time the little plane lands it is completely covered in a thick layer of snow. "This is terrible!" groans the Professor. "The blizzard has blown us off course and I can't tell where we are . . ." Unfolding a map, he shows Rupert the path they were taking and the spot where the Pole should be. "We'll just have to wait till it stops snowing!" he declares. "If we leave the plane now we're bound to get lost. When the blizzard's over I'll use my compass to find the way."

Then, suddenly, a polar bear
Surprises the astonished pair!

It's Rupert's Uncle Polar, who
Lives nearby, in a large igloo . . .

"Come in!" he smiles delightedly.
"You've just dropped by in time for tea!"

Polar agrees to guide the friends.
"We'll set off when this blizzard ends . . ."

Suddenly, Rupert hears someone tapping at the window of the plane. "A wild polar bear!" gasps the Professor. "Uncle Polar!" cries Rupert. "He's not wild. He lives at the North Pole . . ." Rupert's uncle is delighted to see the visitors from Nutwood and invites them to come and shelter in his igloo. "The snowstorm should blow over in a while," he says. "Come and tell me what you're up to!" The Professor blinks in surprise as Polar leads the way across the snow towards his special house . . .

The Professor is even more surprised to see inside the igloo, for Polar's house is far bigger than it seems . . . "Come and have tea!" he says. "It's nice to have guests drop in. I don't get many visitors." When he hears how Nutwood has been covered in ice, Polar agrees that King Frost is the only person who can sort things out. "He lives in a great ice palace, quite near the Pole. I'll take you there when this blizzard stops. It's easy to find when you know the way . . ."

"Clear skies!" smiles Polar. "Time to go!
I'll lead the way across the snow!"

The Professor says he'll fly back
While Rupert goes to visit Jack.

"Jack's father's palace lies nearby
The Northern Lights. Just watch the sky . . ."

"It's like a rainbow!" Rupert blinks.
"And that must be Jack's home!" he thinks.

When everyone has finished tea, Uncle Polar steps outside to see if the blizzard is over. "Clear skies!" he calls. "We won't be troubled again . . ." As Polar knows King Frost, he offers to take Rupert to the ice palace while the Professor flies back to Nutwood. "Good idea!" smiles the Professor. "I'll tell your parents you're in safe hands. If you need any help, just give me a call!" Climbing back into the plane, he starts the engine and is soon soaring off, up into the sky . . .

Uncle Polar sets off towards King Frost's palace. "You'll know we're getting near when you spot the Northern Lights!" he says. "Keep watching until you see the sky change colour . . ." Rupert follows his uncle across the snowy wastes, amazed that he can find the way. "It's my home!" laughs Polar. "In Nutwood, you'd have to show me where to go!" After a while, the sky turns from blue to pink, then to a brilliant green. "Northern Lights!" smiles Polar. "And there's King Frost's palace . . ."

The pair approach a palace where
Two guards stand sentry. "Halt! Who's there?"

"Then Polar mentions King Frost's son
They say he can't see anyone . . .

"I'm sure King Frost will talk to me!
I'd like to see him urgently!"

At last the guard agrees to bring
The pair to see Jack and the King . . .

As they approach the glittering palace, Rupert sees two sentries guarding at the main gate. "Who's there?" they ask. "What business have you with King Frost?" "I've come to see his son," replies Rupert. "Jack and I have often met, during his winter visits to Nutwood . . ." "Young Master Jack is in disgrace for losing his thermometer!" declares the guard. "The King has forbidden him any visitors for the rest of the week. If you want to see him, you'll have to come back later . . ."

"Impossible!" cries Uncle Polar. "Rupert has come here on an urgent mission! Tell King Frost I insist on seeing him." The guard delivers Polar's message and soon comes back to announce that the King will receive them immediately. As he enters the throne room, Rupert spots Jack, still being scolded by his father." "Oh, dear!" he thinks. "I hope he won't be too cross when he hears what's happened. Supposing he decides it serves us right and leaves Nutwood to freeze all winter?"

The King hears how the wand Jack dropped
Will freeze Nutwood unless it's stopped . . .

"Fetch thawing powder straightaway –
We need to act without delay!"

In no time, Jack comes running back
And hands the King a little sack . . .

"Watch!" says King Frost. "This powder's sure
To make the thickest ice all thaw!"

Although King Frost looks cross, he nods to Uncle Polar and asks what brings his nephew all the way to the North Pole. When he hears how the lost thermometer has covered Nutwood in a layer of ice, he shakes his head and declares it is all a result of Jack's carelessness. "You caused the Freeze, so you shall help to end it!" he tells his son. "Fetch a sack of thawing powder from the cellar as quickly as you can. Tell the guards to make sure it's the strongest they can find . . ."

To Rupert's surprise, Jack returns with a small sack, hardly bigger than a bag of flour . . . "Well done!" says the King. "This should soon solve Nutwood's problems, but I'll test a little first, to make sure it works . . ." Taking a pinch of powder from the sack, he sprinkles it on the frozen window-sill. Almost at once, the ice begins to melt, vanishing before Rupert's astonished gaze. "Double strength!" says the King. "Thaws ice and snow in the blink of an eye!"

Rupert and Polar thank the King.
His powder should solve everything.

They say goodbye to Jack Frost too.
"I'll send the wand straight back to you!"

Then Rupert asks his uncle how
He'll travel back to Nutwood now . . .

"Don't worry!" Polar smiles. "You'll see!
There's something you can take for me . . ."

"I knew you would be able to help!" says Polar as he takes the Thawing Powder from King Frost. "We polar bears enjoy ice and snow all year round, but down in Nutwood they don't like being too chilly!" Rupert tells Jack that he'll get his thermometer back for him as soon as the fountain melts. "I'm sure your father won't be cross for long! You didn't mean to freeze Nutwood. It was only an accident, after all!" "Come on!" says Uncle Polar. "It's time we were on our way . . ."

"How am I going to get to Nutwood?" asks Rupert as the pair walk back across the snow. "Will you telephone the Professor and ask him to collect me?" "Don't worry!" laughs Polar. "There's someone else who can take you, even faster than the Professor's plane. We've arranged to meet at my igloo, just after tea-time . . ." As they near Polar's house, Rupert can see no sign of a visitor. "Who is it?" he asks. "You'll see!" smiles his uncle.

RUPERT MEETS SANTA

Rupert tells Polar he can hear
The sound of sleigh bells drawing near . . .

"It's Santa Claus! He's in his sleigh –
Piled high with toys for Christmas Day!"

"Hello!" blinks Santa. "Rupert Bear
From Nutwood! I'm just going there!"

"You'd better fly back home with me!"
The pair take off immediately . . .

The moment they arrive at the igloo, Uncle Polar unlocks a cupboard and reaches inside. "There's a special package I want you to take . . ." he begins but breaks off as Rupert hears the sound of jingling bells. "Look outside!" chuckles Polar. When Rupert crawls out of the igloo he is astonished to see a reindeer-drawn sledge swooping down from the sky. "Santa Claus!" he gasps. "Of course! It's Christmas Eve. He must be on his way to deliver all the children's presents . . ."

Santa is astonished to see Rupert at the North Pole. "I thought you'd be in Nutwood!" he says. "I'm just on my way there to deliver all your presents." "That's why Santa's come visiting!" laughs Polar. "He was going to take a present from me as well . . ." When he hears how Rupert plans to save Nutwood from being buried in ice, Santa agrees to take him there on his sledge. "You're lucky it's the next place on my list," he says. "I hope we won't find it's too icy to land . . ."

RUPERT RETURNS TO NUTWOOD

The sky grows dark and stars come out.
"There won't be anyone about . . ."

They spot the village, down below,
"It looks as if it's thick with snow!"

"The fountain!" Rupert calls. "I'll try
To sprinkle dust as we fly by . . ."

The ice all disappears and then
The fountain starts to work again!

Darkness falls as Santa's reindeer speed on their way to Nutwood. Rupert explains how King Frost has given him a sack full of special powder to thaw the frozen village. "There it is now!" he calls excitedly. "I can see the church tower and everybody's houses . . ." "They should all be tucked up in bed by now," says Santa. "We'll fly over the rooftops and you can sprinkle your powder without being seen. It looks so white and frosty, you'd almost think it had been snowing!"

Santa's sleigh circles over the sleeping village, flying lower and lower, until Rupert spots Nutwood's frozen fountain. Carefully untying King Frost's sack of powder, he reaches over the side and sprinkles a generous handful on the huge mound of ice . . . "I'll land nearby, so we can see if there's any change," announces Santa. By the time the sleigh stops, Rupert is sure he can hear the sound of splashing water. "Look!" he gasps. "It's working! The fountain has thawed already . . ."

RUPERT RECOVERS JACK'S WAND

*"I've got it!" Rupert cries. "Now Jack
Can have his thermometer back!"*

*"Well done! Give me the powder too.
I'll sprinkle all the rest for you!"*

*Next morning, Rupert wakes to find
A present Santa's left behind.*

*"Skates!" Rupert laughs. "Although they're nice
I think we've had enough of ice!"*

Peering into the trough of the fountain, Rupert can see Jack Frost's thermometer, glowing at the bottom. Rolling up his sleeve, he reaches down and lifts it to the surface. "At last!" he cries. "To think it's caused all this trouble . . ." Santa tells Rupert that he will take the thermometer back to Jack when he returns to the North Pole. "I'll take the rest of your powder too," he adds: "I can sprinkle it over Nutwood as I put everyone's presents down the chimney pots."

Next morning, Rupert wakes to find the ice has already melted. At the foot of his bed is a colourful stocking full of presents. "There's the parcel Uncle Polar gave me!" he thinks and hurries to unwrap it straightaway. "Ice skates!" laugh his parents when they see what he has been given. "Normally, I'd wish for a snowy Christmas!" smiles Rupert, "But after all that's happened I don't mind waiting a little while before I try them out . . ." THE END

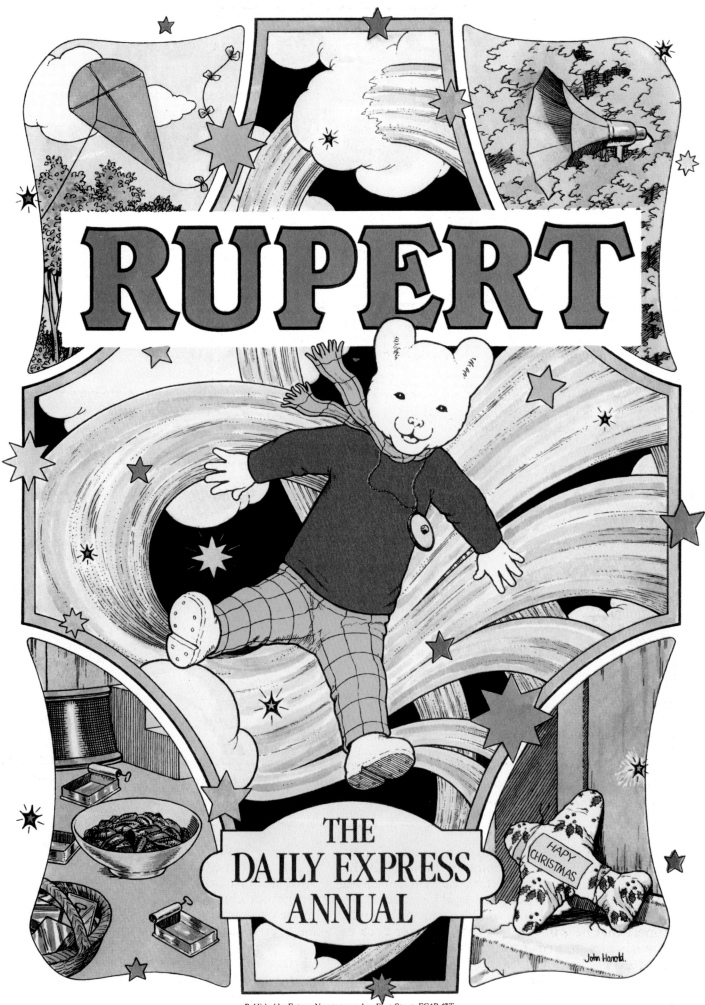

RUPERT

THE
DAILY EXPRESS
ANNUAL

HAPPY CHRISTMAS

John Harold.

Published by Express Newspapers p.l.c., Fleet Street, EC4P 4JT

£3·50